CW00820689

NEW LANCHESTER STRATEGY

NEW LANCHESTER STRATEGY

(The Comic Book)

Shinichi Yano

Ilustrated by Kenichi Sato
Translated by Edwin Delfs

Lanchester Press Incorporated
Sunnyvale California
http://www.lanchester.com

The persons and organizations appearing in this book are fictitious and
have no relation to actual persons or organizations.

© 1990 by SHINICHI YANO/KENICHI SATO, Japan
English Language Edition © 1995 by Lanchester Press Inc.
Reprinted with permission of Lanchester Strategic Management Institute, Tokyo.

All rights reserved, including the right of reproduction in whole or in part by any means.

ISBN 1-57321-000-5 1995

Library of Congress Catalog Card Number: 95-77646

Editor: John Schuler
Electronic imaging by Costas Schuler
Translation from Japanese by Edwin Delfs
Printed and bound by Patson's Press, Sunnyvale, California
Lanchester Press Inc. P.O. Box 60621, Sunnyvale, CA 94086, U.S.A.

Contents

A Note on the English Edition

The conventional wisdom is that the Japanese economic juggernaut has been powered by low interest rates and fastidious attention to quality. However, several million books published in Japan on the Lanchester strategy of market share has, without doubt, had a significant effect.

We are pleased to offer this first volume of a series of works by Shinichi Yano to the English speaking audience. We believe that these works are of interest for the following three reasons:

Firstly, as an insight into tactics and strategy of market share domination as practiced with much success by Japanese companies.

Secondly, we believe that this work breaks new ground as a serious book on marketing theory in the "manga" or comic book form.

And finally, we are pleased to introduce to a wider audience the works of F. W. Lanchester, whose pioneering book "Aircraft in Warfare" forms the basis of the Lanchester strategy of market share.

John Schuler
Editor

INTRODUCTION

The Japanese proponent of the Lanchester Strategy, Dr. Nobuo Taoka, who passed away in 1984, first encountered the Lanchester laws in 1960. Through Taoka's subsequent research, Lanchester's theories were reborn as a sales strategy perfectly suited to Japan's business climate.

The Lanchester Strategy has been used as a sales strategy for more than 20 years, and it remains as valid as ever. In fact, recently an increasing number of companies have been turning to the Lanchester strategy, part of the current trend to "get back to the basics," because the principles of competition do not change.

However, markets do change, and they have changed over the past 20 years. Some aspects of the strategy are no longer in keeping with actual market conditions, an inevitable situation. For that reason, we have expanded upon the original Lanchester Strategy and revised portions of it that have been misunderstood, thus providing a strategy more suited to the "battles" we face and easier to implement. We have christened the revised version the "New Lanchester Strategy."

We have issued this book in *manga*, or comic-book format, for the following reasons:

    1. Most of the writings about sales strategy and marketing, and the theories presented in those writings, have come into Japan from the U.S. They are not easily understandable, possibly because the target audience has generally been business owners or managers.

    2. We wanted to make this book accessible to the younger generation. The Lanchester Strategy is simply a basic strategy. Companies must customize it to fit their individual situations. The adaptation process requires new ideas, ideas unhampered by convention. Regardless of how talented they are, as people age and gain experience, they tend to lose the ability to think flexibly. We have entered the age of the unknown. In this time of turmoil, we need to arm ourselves with new ideas and theories.

3. Since the New Lanchester Strategy differs from the original Lanchester Strategy, it is necessary to describe it in different terms. However, even though we have used the comic-book format, this book is certainly not a digest or summary. It was our intention in presenting the fundamentals of the Lanchester Strategy in three volumes, to describe it in more detail than was provided in previous writings on the subject.

Volume 1 of *The New Lanchester Strategy* contains five chapters. Chapter One outlines the history of the Lanchester strategy. Chapter Two describes the Lanchester laws, the basis for the strategy of the strong and the strategy of the weak. Chapter Three focuses on market share targets and the shooting range theory extrapolated from the Lanchester Strategy model. In the summary at the end of Chapter 3, we include the equations for deriving 40% and $\sqrt{3}$, with which many people have had difficulty.

In Chapter Four, we provide a detailed explanation of the three main points of the New Lanchester Strategy, which forms the framework of this series. Chapter Five discusses the applications of the Lanchester Strategy to tactical strength, providing a scientific explanation of offensive strength in terms of flyers and direct mail, with emphasis on sales activities.

The first part of each chapter is in comic-book format, followed by a text summary. Anyone who reads this book from start to finish should be able to understand the basics of the Lanchester Strategy.

Shinichi Yano
Tokyo, Japan
1986

CHAPTER ONE

THE LANCHESTER STRATEGY

OUR CAST OF CHARACTERS

Shinsaku Sakamoto
The hero of our story.

Supervisor of Section 3,
Sales Dept. Company W.

Has doubts about current
company strategy and is
determined to convince
his supervisors to
implement the Lanchester
Strategy . . . .

Taizo Masumura
Director of Company W.

Dedicated to his work, but angered by his department's poor performance. Has heard about the power of Lanchester Strategy, but is not totally convinced . . .

Motoharu Ohashi
Manager of Section 3

Also has doubts about the company strategy, but knocks himself out trying to meet his quotas. Interested in Lanchester Strategy, and is sympathetic to our hero.

Yuji Kondo
Chief Salesman of Section 3

Colleague and rival of our hero and critical of the Lanchester Strategy .

Supervisor Nishiyama, Colleague of our hero

Supervisor Oda, Colleague of our hero

Analyst Rumiko Kawano who supports our hero

Salesman Mori, Reports to our hero but supports Kondo

3

WHAT'S THE MATTER WITH YOU GUYS? HAVE YOU LOST YOUR WILL?

THREE CONSECUTIVE PERIODS OF NEGATIVE RESULTS. THE COMPANY IS LOSING CONFIDENCE IN OUR ABILITY...!

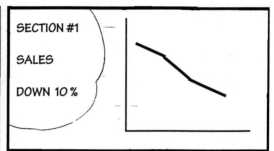

SECTION #1

SALES

DOWN 10%

WHY DID I BOTHER TO SET TARGETS?

SECTION 2, DID EVEN WORSE...!!

SO .... SORRY

5

THE SAKAMOTO TEAM'S SALES INCREASED, SO OVERALL THE SECTION RESULTS REMAINED LEVEL.

I THINK SAKAMOTO SHOULD EXPLAIN, SINCE HE'S THE TEAM LEADER

FINE...

IS SAKAMOTO HERE?

YES!

I

AM

HERE

I AM SAKAMOTO

.....

7

10

THAT BUTTHEAD KONDO IS ALWAYS BUTTING IN...

I UNDERSTAND, BUT SOME PEOPLE HERE MAY NOT UNDERSTAND SOME CRITICAL POINTS OF THE STRATEGY

EVERYBODY HERE IS VERY BUSY....

..SO MAKE IT SNAPPY!

CALM DOWN, KONDO!

I THINK WE SHOULD LET SAKAMOTO EXPLAIN

INDEED, THERE MAY BE SOME OF US HERE WHO KNOW NOTHING OF THIS FELLOW LANCHESTER

IF SAKAMOTO USED THIS STRATEGY TO BOOST SALES, WE SHOULD LISTEN. BESIDES, IT'S AN INTERESTING TOPIC...

MR. LANCH-ESTER ⌐

HOW IS THE ENGINE DESIGN COMING ALONG?

JUST FINE SIR ..

14

THAT'S THE GASOLINE-POWERED CAR THAT LANCHESTER DESIGNED

OK...
IT'S FINISHED

LET'S DO A TEST RUN..

I HOPE IT WORKS

VROOOMMM...!!!

WOW!!!

GREAT JOB LANCHESTER. GIVE US A RIDE !

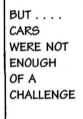

BUT . . . .
CARS
WERE NOT
ENOUGH
OF A
CHALLENGE

. . PLANES . .

THE FIRST WORLD WAR BROKE OUT IN 1914....

LANCHESTER WAS COMPLETELY ABSORBED IN HIS AERONAUTICS RESEARCH...

IN THIS WAR THE SKIES WILL BE THE BATTLEFIELDS....

AIRCRAFT PERFORMANCE WILL HAVE A MAJOR EFFECT ON THE OUTCOME

I NEED TO THINK ABOUT WING DESIGN AND THE PROPELLERS

LANCHESTER HAD ALREADY MADE MAJOR THEORETICAL AND PRACTICAL CONTRIBUTIONS TO AERONAUTICAL ENGINEERING, ONE OF THEM WAS HIS BOOK "AERODYNAMICS"

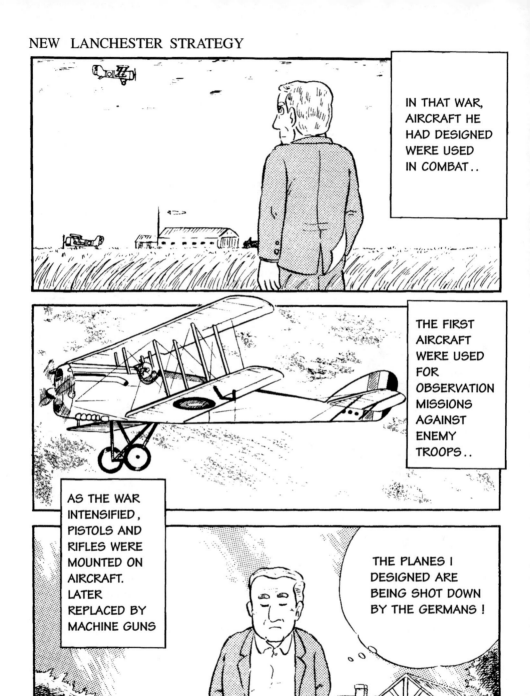

IN THAT WAR, AIRCRAFT HE HAD DESIGNED WERE USED IN COMBAT..

THE FIRST AIRCRAFT WERE USED FOR OBSERVATION MISSIONS AGAINST ENEMY TROOPS..

AS THE WAR INTENSIFIED, PISTOLS AND RIFLES WERE MOUNTED ON AIRCRAFT. LATER REPLACED BY MACHINE GUNS

THE PLANES I DESIGNED ARE BEING SHOT DOWN BY THE GERMANS!

I WONDER...?

HOW CAN A STRONGER ENEMY BE DEFEATED BY AN INFERIOR FORCE ?

IS THERE A RELATIONSHIP BETWEEN THE NUMBER OF PLANES ON THE TWO SIDES AND THE NUMBER OF CASUALTIES

NOW, LET'S SEE.. IN THIS BATTLE, SEVEN OF OUR PLANES WERE SHOT DOWN..

THE ENEMY ONLY LOST THREE

THAT BOY NEVER SEEMS TO SLEEP. WHAT KIND OF RESEARCH IS HE WORKING ON NOW?

19

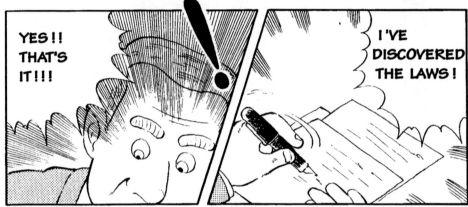

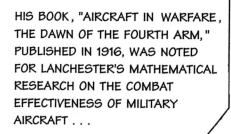

HIS BOOK, "AIRCRAFT IN WARFARE, THE DAWN OF THE FOURTH ARM," PUBLISHED IN 1916, WAS NOTED FOR LANCHESTER'S MATHEMATICAL RESEARCH ON THE COMBAT EFFECTIVENESS OF MILITARY AIRCRAFT . . .

PROPOSALS FROM THIS BOOK LED TO THE ESTABLISHMENT OF THE ROYAL AIR FORCE AND THE AIR MINISTRY IN 1918

THE LANCHESTER LAWS WERE LATER EXPANDED INTO A MODEL BY DR. B. O. KOOPMAN, AN AMERICAN MATHEMATICIAN, AND OTHERS.
THE MODEL WAS USED SUCCESSFULLY IN THE SECOND WORLD WAR.

SO... THERE YOU HAVE IT, THE HIGHLIGHTS OF LANCHESTER'S CAREER

HERE IN JAPAN, A CONSULTANT, DR. NOBUO TAOKA, DEVELOPED A SALES STRATEGY BASED ON THE LANCHESTER STRATEGY. HE EXPANDED THE AREAS OF APPLICATION AND WROTE MORE THAN 20 BOOKS ABOUT IT.

IT IS FROM THESE BOOKS THAT I LEARNED ABOUT LANCHESTER

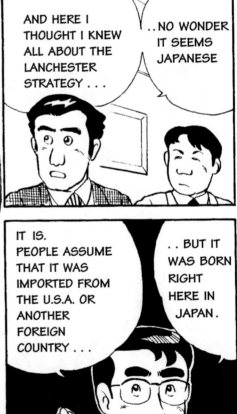

AND HERE I THOUGHT I KNEW ALL ABOUT THE LANCHESTER STRATEGY...

..NO WONDER IT SEEMS JAPANESE

IT IS. PEOPLE ASSUME THAT IT WAS IMPORTED FROM THE U.S.A. OR ANOTHER FOREIGN COUNTRY...

.. BUT IT WAS BORN RIGHT HERE IN JAPAN.

23

HOW LONG IS THAT IDIOT GOING TO GO ON LIKE THIS!

ENOUGH BOASTING. GET ON WITH THE STORY!

EXCUSE ME! I GOT CARRIED AWAY

ANYWAY, . . . REMEMBER THAT THE LANCHESTER STRATEGY SUPPLIES ONLY THE BASICS

TO EFFECTIVELY PUT THESE PRINCIPLES INTO PRACTICE, COMPANIES MUST TAILOR THE BASIC CONCEPTS TO THEIR OWN NEED

WE WORKED OUT A NEW INTERPRETATION OF THE ORIGINAL LANCHESTER STRATEGY, WHICH WE'VE BEEN IMPLEMENTING. WE CALL IT THE **NEW LANCHESTER STRATEGY**.

25

I THINK YOUR SALES RESULTS WERE A FLUKE!

THANKS TO YOU WE HAD SUCH A LONG MEETING TODAY !

MY TEAM WILL OUTSELL YOURS BEFORE YOU KNOW IT!

THE DIRECTOR HAS NO INTENTION OF ADOPTING THE LANCHESTER STRATEGY!

HMMM..

?

SAKAMOTO

27

YES, MR. OHASHI

MR. SAKAMOTO, DON'T BE IMPATIENT

I AM INTERESTED IN LEARNING MORE ABOUT THE LANCHESTER STRATEGY

I AGREE WITH YOU.

BUT IT'S TOO SOON, YOU'LL HAVE TO PROVE THAT IT WORKS FIRST.

YES SIR

ALL RIGHT! I'M GOING TO DO IT! THEN EVERYONE WILL BE MORE RECEPTIVE TO THE NEW LANCHESTER STRATEGY.

28

SUMMARY

The Lanchester Strategy is based on the Lanchester laws, discovered by the British aeronautical engineer, F.W. Lanchester. Lanchester was born on October 23, 1868, in London. He graduated from the Royal College of Science. At the age of 28, he designed and built England's first gasoline-powered automobile. At 31, he founded a consulting firm, the Lanchester Car Company. Subsequently, he was a member of the Advisory Committee for Aeronautics, and a technical advisor to Daimler Co., Ltd. He was also a member of the British Academy, a Doctor of Laws, and an honorary member of the Royal Aeronautical Society.

Lanchester's career ended on March 8, 1946, with his death in Birmingham, northwest of London. A museum has been built in his memory in nearby Coventry. One room in that museum is devoted to exhibits of Lanchester's writings and personal papers.

His research paper entitled " *The Theory of Rotation and Lift*" and a two-volume treatise on aerodynamics, " *Aerial Flight* ," were published in 1907. These writings reportedly were major contributions to aeronautical science at the time.

The ideas proposed in these works were later incorporated into airfoil theory by the German physicist Ludwig Prandtl, and are still used today, known as the Lanchester-Prandtl Three-Dimensional Airfoil Theory.

After the outbreak of World War I in 1914, Lanchester, with great interest, witnessed battles in which aircraft he had worked on were used. He became convinced of the need for a mathematical analysis of the relative strengths of opposing battlefield forces to describe the effectiveness of aircraft. By doing quantitative studies of the number of casualties on both sides in land, sea, and air battles, he arrived at the Lanchester laws.

I lis findings are recorded in *"Aircraft in Warfare , the Dawn of the Fourth Arm,"* which he published in 1916. Lanchester's quantitative and mathematical studies of the affect of aircraft on combat were the first of their kind and attracted a great deal of attention. His book emphasized the importance of an air force's role in military strategy of the future. His suggestions were adopted by Major-General Henderson, with the result that the Royal Air Force and the Air Ministry were established.

Subsequently, the laws discovered by Lanchester were studied further in the U.S. They were used with overwhelming success in military strategy in the latter stages of World II, including landing operations in the Central Pacific.

Lanchester's work was introduced into Japan in 1952 in a book on OR (Operations Research) sent by the quality authority, W. Edward Deming.

In 1960, Saburkita, then manager of the Japanese Economic Planning Agency's Policy Bureau, collaborated with some of his ministry colleagues on a book. One chapter, "Applying the Lanchester Laws to Corporate Competition," cites Lanchester's work, but mentions only that the most powerful competitor wins.

It was Dr. Nobuo Taoka who applied Lanchester's theories to sales strategy. Taoka died suddenly on November 23, 1984, but from 1962 until his death, he studied Lanchester's ideas and restructured Lanchester's military and OR strategies into a sales strategy.

This sales strategy was lauded for dispensing with the traditional idealism and spirit, and for being a scientific, realistic sales strategy. The books that Taoka wrote about the strategy were unprecedented best sellers in the business category in Japan.

CHAPTER TWO

LANCHESTER'S FIRST AND SECOND LAWS

MR. SAKAMOTO, WE RECEIVED AN ORDER FROM THE HANADA COMPANY

REALLY ? !

GOOD WORK !

YOUR PERSISTENCE PAID OFF, I'M PROUND OF YOU, MATSUDA

MR. MORI, HOW ARE YOUR PEOPLE DOING?

WELL, WE'RE TRYING HARD, BUT IT'S AN UPHILL BATTLE

OUR RIVAL, COMPANY B, IS MAKING THINGS DIFFICULT

KEEP AT IT! I TAUGHT YOU HOW TO USE THE LANCHESTER STRATEGY DIDN'T I?

YES... YOU DID I'M SORRY.

ALL I HEAR IS THAT DAMN LANCHESTER,.. LANCHESTER

I WON'T LET HIM GET AWAY WITH THIS.

JUST WAIT, MR. KONDO'S GOING TO ZOOM AHEAD OF SAKAMOTO

CHIEF . . . I'D LIKE TO PAY A VISIT TO THE YOSHIMOTO COMPANY

WEREN'T YOU OVER THERE JUST THE OTHER DAY ?

YES, BUT I'VE GOT A HUNCH - JUST A SMALL ONE THOUGH.

YOU DO ? REALLY ! !

I'LL CONVINCE THEM TO BUY FROM US, I PROMISE.

34

THESE DAYS MR. SAKAMOTO LOOKS SO HANDSOME AND SELF-ASSURED

UH-OH. YOU'D BETTER WATCH OUT, RUMIKO

FORGET HIM,

HE HAS A WIFE AND KIDS.

WHAT?!

YOU'RE KIDDING!

ITS NOT ONLY HIS WORK HE CARES ABOUT, HE IS DEVOTED TO HIS FAMILY

OH? THAT'S NICE! I'M REALLY ATTRACTED TO HIM.

IT'S HOPELESS SHE'S HOOKED

35

THANKS TO THE EFFORTS OF KONDO AND SAKAMOTO, SECTION 3'S PERFORMANCE GRADUALLY IMPROVES.

DEPT 3

HOW DID KONDO'S TEAM DO SO WELL?

HOW DID HE DO IT?

I HEARD HE PICKED UP SOME BUSINESS FROM A COMPANY WHERE ONE OF HIS RELATIVES WORKS

SO,... IT WAS CONNECTIONS!

CONNECTIONS OR NOT, IT'S THE RESULTS THAT COUNT.

YOU DID IT MR. KONDO!

36

CONFERENCE
ROOM

THERE'S AN
ASPECT OF
SECTION 3'S
WORK THAT WE
SHOULD TAKE
A CLOSE LOOK AT.

ACCORDING
TO THE RESULTS,
KONDO'S TEAM
WON . . . .

BUT I WAS SURPRISED
TO SEE HOW WELL
SAKAMOTO'S TEAM
DID IN THE NEW
TERRITORY.

38

IT SEEMS THAT SAKAMOTO IS THE RESIDENT EXPERT ON THE LANCHESTER STRATEGY

EXPLAIN IT SO WE CAN ALL UNDERSTAND IT.

THERE'S PLENTY OF TIME.

I'VE ALREADY TOLD YOU ABOUT LANCHESTER THE MAN

NOW I'D LIKE TO TELL YOU ABOUT HIS STRATEGY

YES SIR !

I WILL BE PLEASED TO ASSIST

AS SOME OF YOU KNOW,

THE LANCHESTER STRATEGY COMPRISES TWO LAWS . . .

THE FIRST LAW AND THE SECOND LAW

$$Mo-M=E(No-N)$$

Mo·· INITIAL NUMERICAL STRENGTH (ARMY M)

M··· FINAL NUMERICAL STRENGTH (ARMY M)

E··· EXCHANGE RATE WEAPON EFFICIENCY
(PERFORMANCE OF WEAPONS,
SKILL OF USERS)

No·· INITIAL NUMERICAL STRENGTH (ARMY N)

N··· FINAL NUMERICAL STRENGTH (ARMY N)

COMBAT STRENGTH = **E** × [NUMERICAL STRENGTH]

41

WHEN PRIMITIVE WEAPONS SUCH AS THE BOW AND ARROW AND SPEARS ARE USED, AS IN ANCIENT TIMES . . . .

AND WEAPON EFFICIENCY IS EQUAL ON BOTH SIDES (E = 1), THE INITIAL NUMERICAL STRENGTH DETERMINES THE NUMBER OF CASUALTIES

Mo···5 SOLDIERS

No···3 SOLDIERS

$5 - M = 1 \times (3 - 0)$

$M = 5 - 3$

$M = 2$

ARMY M IS LEFT WITH 2 SURVIVORS

IF ARMY M HAS 5 MEN, AND ARMY N 3, THIS IS WHAT HAPPENS ACCORDING TO THE EQUATION

WHEN E = 1, THE LARGER ARMY WINS, WITH THE NUMBER OF ITS SURVIVORS BEING EQUAL TO ITS NUMERICAL SUPERIORITY

ARMY M		ARMY N
A	———————	A
B	———————	B
C	———————	C
D	SURVIVORS	
E		

SO, WHAT DOES ARMY N NEED TO DO IN ORDER TO WIN IN BATTLE AGAINST ARMY M?

IT NEEDS TO RAISE ITS WEAPON EFFICIENCY (E)

THE RATIO, 5 MEN TO 3 MEN, IS ABOUT 1.7, SO IT NEEDS ITS MEN WITH WEAPONS THAT ARE 1.7 TIMES MORE EFFECTIVE, OR TRAIN THEM TO IMPROVE THEIR SKILLS BY 1.7 TIMES

ARMY N NEEDS TO INCREASE ITS EFFECTIVE STRENGTH TO THE EQUIVALENT OF AT LEAST FIVE MEN

WHAT YOU SAID IS ABSOLUTELY RIGHT !

THE JAPANESE COMMANDER TAKEDA SHINGEN USED CAVALRY TO ADVANTAGE

ANOTHER COMMANDER, ODA NOBUNAGA WON BY USING GUNS

44

IN EFFECT, THEY INCREASED WEAPON EFFICIENCY (E)

TOYOTOMI HIDEYOSHI WAS ONE COMMANDER WHO BELIEVED IN STRENGTH IN NUMBERS

OH !
I THINK I
UNDERSTAND
NOW

THUS . . .
LAW NO. 1 IS
THE BASIS FOR
THE "STRATEGY
OF THE WEAK"

NOW . . .
LET'S TAKE A
LOOK AT LAW
NO. 2

IT'S A BIT
MORE COMPLEX
THAN THE
FIRST LAW.

LAW NO. 1 IS
APPLIED TO
SINGLE COMBAT
WHERE AIM IS
IMPORTANT

WHILE LAW NO. 2
IS APPLIED TO COMBAT
WHERE MODERN
WEAPONS, WHICH,
FIRE AT RANDOM
ARE USED.

47

$$Mo^2 - M^2 = E(No^2 - N^2)$$

Mo · · INITIAL NUMERICAL STRENGTH (ARMY M)

M · · · FINAL NUMERICAL STRENGTH (ARMY M)

E · · · · · exchange rate

(WEAPON EFFICIENCY, PERFORMANCE
OF WEAPONS, SKILL OF USERS)

No · · INITIAL NUMERICAL STRENGTH (ARMY N)

N · · · FINAL NUMERICAL STRENGTH (ARMY N)

COMBAT STRENGTH $= E \times [\text{NUMERICAL STRENGTH}]^2$

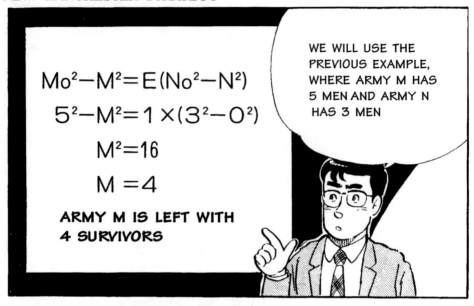

$$Mo^2 - M^2 = E(No^2 - N^2)$$
$$5^2 - M^2 = 1 \times (3^2 - 0^2)$$
$$M^2 = 16$$
$$M = 4$$

ARMY M IS LEFT WITH 4 SURVIVORS

WE WILL USE THE PREVIOUS EXAMPLE, WHERE ARMY M HAS 5 MEN AND ARMY N HAS 3 MEN

WHY DID THE RESULTS TURN OUT LIKE THIS?

WHEN WE APPLIED THE FIRST LAW, 2 MEN REMAINED, BUT WITH THE SECOND LAW, 4 MEN REMAIN.

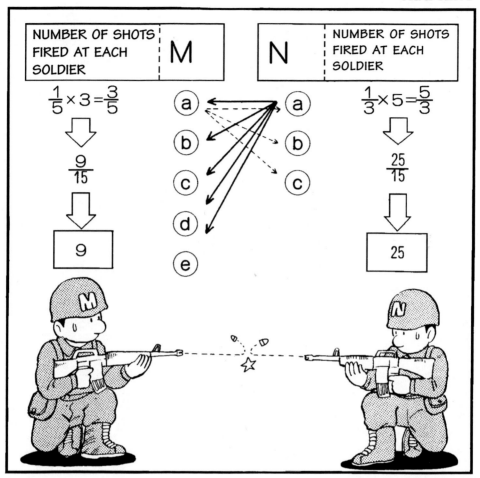

NUMBER OF SHOTS FIRED AT EACH SOLDIER

M

N

NUMBER OF SHOTS FIRED AT EACH SOLDIER

$$\frac{1}{5} \times 3 = \frac{3}{5}$$

$$\frac{9}{15}$$

9

$$\frac{1}{3} \times 5 = \frac{5}{3}$$

$$\frac{25}{15}$$

25

SINCE SOLDIER A FROM ARMY M ATTACKS EACH SOLDIER A, B, AND C OF ARMY N, EACH WILL RECEIVE ONE-THIRD OF THE TOTAL ASSAULT. BECAUSE ARMY M HAS FIVE MEN, THE MAGNITUDE OF THE ASSAULT RECEIVED BY EACH MAN IN THE N ARMY IS 5/3

SINCE SOLDIER A FROM ARMY N ATTACKS EACH SOLDIER A, B, C, D, AND E OF ARMY M, EACH WILL RECEIVE ONE-FIFTH OF THE TOTAL ASSAULT. BECAUSE ARMY N HAS THREE MEN, THE MAGNITUDE OF THE ASSAULT RECEIVED BY EACH MAN IN THE M ARMY IS 3/5

① INCREASE THE STRENGTH (TO AT LEAST 5)

② IMPROVE WEAPON EFFICIENCY (E)

$$\frac{5^2}{3^2} = \frac{25}{9} = 2.8 \quad 2.8 \text{ MULTIPLIER}$$

USE WEAPONS THAT ARE 2.8 TIMES AS EFFEC-
TIVE OR INCREASE SKILL LEVELS SO THAT THE
USE OF EXISTING WEAPONS IS IMPROVED BY
A FACTOR OF AT LEAST 2.8

THIS PAGE IS FOR ALL WHO TOOK LONGER THAN 3 MINUTES . . .

LET'S WORK ON THIS TOGETHER

FIRST . . . LET'S DETERMINE WEAPON EFFICIENCY (E)

N 800 ROUNDS/MINUTE

M 100 ROUNDS/MINUTE

$$E = \frac{800}{100} = 8$$

DID YOU TRY SOLVING IT USING THE METHOD SHOWN BELOW ?

NOW ..

IF YOU TRY TO SOLVE FOR TWO UNKNOWNS (M AND N) WITH ONLY ONE EQUATION, YOU WON'T BE SUCCESSFUL.

$$Mo^2 - M^2 = E(No^2 - N^2)$$

$$9^2 - M^2 = 8(3^2 - N^2)$$

WHO AM I ?

54

	ARMY M		ARMY N
E	1	:	8
RATIO OF STRENGTH	9	:	1

RATIO OF STRENGTH IS
9 : 3 OR 3 : 1

THIS IS LAW NO. 2, SO THE RESULT GETS SQUARED.

FIRST . . . YOU NEED TO DECIDE WHICH FORCE WILL WIN

M = 9

N = 8

SO ARMY M WILL WIN

THEREFORE, N = 0 SO APPLYING THIS TO THE EQUATION FOR LAW NO. 2

USUALLY ONLY 10 % GET IT RIGHT THE FIRST TIME

DON'T TAKE IT TO HEART !

YOU ARE IN THE 90 % GROUP !

$$Mo^2 - M^2 = E(No^2 - N^2)$$

$$9^2 - M^2 = 8(3^2 - 0^2)$$

$$M^2 = 9^2 - 8 \times 3^2$$

$$= 9$$

$$M = 3$$

ANSWER : ARMY M WINS WITH THREE MEN LEFT !

ANSWER

ARMY M WINS
—
3 MEN REMAIN

FIRST, LET'S VERIFY THE SOLUTION

READ THIS IF YOU GOT THE ANSWER

GOOD JOB !

APPROACH

$$E = \frac{800}{100} = 8$$

YOU NEED TO DETERMINE THE WINNER

ARMY M		ARMY N	
E	1	:	8
	9	:	1 STRENGTH RATIO

RATIO OF STRENGTH IS 9 : 3 OR 3 : 1 THIS IS LAW NO. 2, SO THE RESULT GETS SQUARED

NOW YOU SEE THAT ARMY M WINS ! !

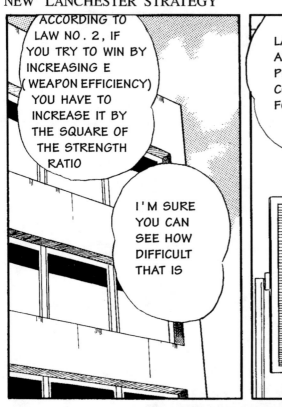

ACCORDING TO LAW NO. 2, IF YOU TRY TO WIN BY INCREASING E (WEAPON EFFICIENCY) YOU HAVE TO INCREASE IT BY THE SQUARE OF THE STRENGTH RATIO

I'M SURE YOU CAN SEE HOW DIFFICULT THAT IS

LAW NO. 2 APPLIES TO PRESENT-DAY COMPETITION FOR MARKETS

REMEMBER THAT RAISING MARKET SHARE (NUMERICAL STRENGTH) EVEN A LITTLE PUTS YOU IN A GOOD POSITION

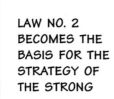

LAW NO. 2 BECOMES THE BASIS FOR THE STRATEGY OF THE STRONG

ARE THERE ANY QUESTIONS ABOUT WHAT WE'VE COVERED SO FAR?

YES !
I HAVE A
QUESTION

OH, NO . . .
IT'S KONDO

I THINK I
KNOW A FAIR
AMOUNT ABOUT
THE
LANCHESTER
STRATEGY

I'M CONVINCED
THAT IT'S THE
STRATEGY OF
THE STRONG

IN THE EXAMPLE
YOU SHOWED,
THE 5-MAN
ARMY WILL WIN
EVERY
TIME

I AM
OF THE
SAME
OPINION . .

I DON'T
THINK OUR
COMPANY
CAN USE IT

I ADMIT THAT PEOPLE TEND TO MISUNDERSTAND THIS ASPECT . . . .

LET ME EXPLAIN IT IN TERMS OF THE BATTLE OF TRAFALGAR

TRA . . . WHAT ?

TRAFALGAR, FOR HEAVEN'S SAKE ! !

SPAIN

PORTUGAL

CAPE TRAFALGAR

IN 1805, AT THE CAPE OF TRAFALGAR, THE BRITISH FLEET FOUGHT A COMBINED FRENCH - SPANISH FLEET IN ONE OF THE MOST FAMOUS BATTLES IN HISTORY

THIS BATTLE MARKED THE BEGINNING OF NAPOLEON'S DECLINE

AFTER WHICH, ENGLAND TOOK CONTROL OF THE SEAS . .

THE SMALLER FLEET WON THE BATTLE

WE SHOULD TAKE A CLOSE LOOK AT THIS FAMOUS BATTLE, AS THE WEAKER SIDE WON A TREMENDOUS VICTORY . . .

THE COMBINED FRENCH - SPANISH FLEET HAD 33 SHIPS THE BRITISH HAD ONLY 27 . . . .

REALIZING THAT IF THE FLEETS MET HEAD ON, THE ENGLISH WOULD BE EASILY DEFEATED . . ADMIRAL NELSON MADE A PLAN . . .

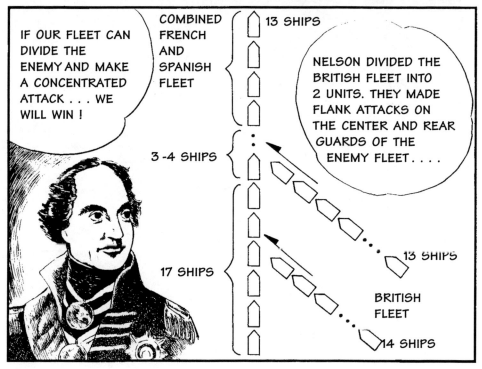

IF OUR FLEET CAN DIVIDE THE ENEMY AND MAKE A CONCENTRATED ATTACK . . . WE WILL WIN !

COMBINED FRENCH AND SPANISH FLEET

13 SHIPS

3 -4 SHIPS

17 SHIPS

NELSON DIVIDED THE BRITISH FLEET INTO 2 UNITS. THEY MADE FLANK ATTACKS ON THE CENTER AND REAR GUARDS OF THE ENEMY FLEET. . . .

13 SHIPS

BRITISH FLEET

14 SHIPS

61

THE ENEMY'S ADVANCE GUARD WAS UNABLE TO TAKE PART IN THE FIRST ENGAGEMENT

SO . . . 27 BRITISH SHIPS FOUGHT AGAINST 20-21 ENEMY SHIPS

AFTER DEFEATING THE FIRST 20 SHIPS, NELSON'S FLEET ATTACKED THE REMAINING 12-13 SHIPS . . . THE OUTCOME . . .

BRITISH FLEET:
    27 SHIPS AT OUTSET
    NONE SUNK

COMBINED FLEET:
    33 SHIPS AT OUTSET
    22 CAPTURED OR SUNK
    11 SHIPS ESCAPED

THE WEAKER FORCE CAN WIN WITH A STRATEGY LIKE THIS

WELL . . . . .UHM . . WHEN YOU PUT IT THAT WAY !

IN THAT BATTLE, NELSON WAS HIT BY A MUSKET BALL, AND DIED FROM HIS WOUNDS, HIS LAST WORDS, WHICH HAVE BECAME FAMOUS, WERE "THANK GOD, I HAVE DONE MY DUTY." HERE WAS A COMMANDER WHO TRULY DESERVED HIS VICTORY.

63

SUMMARY

Lanchester discovered two laws, Lanchester's first law and Lanchester's second law, by analyzing land, sea, and air battles. The laws are also known as Lanchester's Linear Law (Law No. 1) and Lanchester's Square Law (Law No. 2). These names were not used by Lanchester, but were adopted later by the U.S. Navy's Operations Research Team (see below).

Lanchester's First Law

Lanchester's first law is often referred to as the "Law of Single Combat," since it concerns combat between individuals. Weapons used in ancient times (swords, spears, and bows and arrows) were designed for single combat. No matter how large the forces were, the battles fought then were simply a series of concurrent duels.

In a battle of this type, the outcome hinges on the difference between initial numerical strength on the opposing sides. The ancient Chinese treatise on battle strategy, written by Sun Tzu, gives the following advice: "If the strength of your army is equal to that of the enemy, fight bravely. If it is weaker than that of the enemy, then retreat."

The famous Prussian military strategist Von Clausewitz provides further advice: "Superior military strength is the most important factor in determining the outcome of a battle. At the basis of strategy is the theory that the force with the largest numbers wins."

Lanchester used the following equation to describe single-combat battles: If $E = 1$ (weapon performance and users' skills are the same on both sides), then in order to annihilate the enemy,
$M_0 - M = N_0$, or $M_0 - N_0 = M$.

For instance, when the five-man Army M battles the three-man Army N, we have $5 - 3 = 2$. After Army N has been annihilated, Army M is left with two survivors. In other words, the numerically superior side wins,

LANCHESTER'S FIRST LAW

$$M_0 - M = E(N_0 - N)$$

M_0 = INITIAL NUMERICAL STRENGTH (ARMY M)

M = FINAL NUMERICAL STRENGTH (ARMY M)

E = EXCHANGE RATE (WEAPON EFFICIENCY *)

N_0 = INITIAL NUMERICAL STRENGTH (ARMY N)

N = FINAL NUMERICAL STRENGTH (ARMY N)

COMBAT STRENGTH = E × [NUMERICAL STRENGTH]

* LANCHESTER MENTIONED ONLY WEAPON PERFORMANCE, BUT IT IS UNWISE TO NEGLECT SKILL AND MORALE.

LANCHESTER'S SECOND LAW

$$M_0^2 - M^2 = E(N_0^2 - N^2)$$

COMBAT STRENGTH = E × [NUMERICAL STRENGTH]^2

and the number of its survivors is equal to the amount by which it is numerically superior to its enemy.

To win a battle of the single-combat type, there are two basic requirements:

1 Increase numerical strength
2 Raise E (weapon efficiency)

The side with inferior numerical strength must possess efficient weapons, or raise the skills of those who use them, i.e., increase E, in order to win a battle. If that is not possible, another option is to increase E by resorting to feint operations, e.g., making a concentrated attack somewhere on the enemy lines, or lowering the enemy's morale. In summary, Lanchester's first law is the basis for the "Strategy of the Weak."

Lanchester's Second Law

The second law addresses battles between groups, and is commonly referred to as the "Law of Stochastic Warfare" or the "Law of Concentration."

Since the variables are squared, it is also known as the "Square Law." The second law is better known than the first. And because cannons and machine guns are used in battles between groups, the battle covers a wider area, and probability becomes a factor.

Lanchester represented this type of stochastic combat as follows: If $E = 1$, to annihilate the enemy, $M_0^2 - M^2 = N_0^2$, or $M_0^2 - N_0^2 = M^2$.

If the five-man Army M battles the three-man army N, then we have $5^2 - 3^2 = 16 = 4^2$. When Army N has been annihilated, Army M is left with four survivors.

In the previous example demonstrating Lanchester's first law, only two men remained. Therefore, it is much more advantageous for the army with numerical superiority to conduct a battle in accordance with the second law.

A two-fold strength ratio yields a four-fold difference, and a 3-fold strength ratio yields a nine-fold difference. The Navy reportedly referred to this law as the "N^2 Law."

This law became the starting point for Operations Research (OR). In the U.S., a Lanchester Prize has been established. A prize is awarded to distinguished OR researchers annually.

To win wide-area, stochastic battles, it is important to follow the same principles laid out in the first law:

    1 Increase numerical strength
    2 Increase E

However, in this case, E must be increased in proportion to the square of the strength ratio. Since in today's world, it is not easy to raise E, one option for the army with inferior numerical strength is to decrease the enemy's combat strength by dispersing its troops (this is the strategy Admiral Nelson adopted in the Battle of Trafalgar. Lanchester mentions that battle in his book, *Aircraft in Warfare the Dawn of the Fourth Arm*).

Lanchester's second law formed the basis for the "Strategy of the Strong," which was formulated at a later date.

CHAPTER THREE

THE LANCHESTER STRATEGY MODEL

THE LANCHESTER STRATEGY MODEL TAKES INTO ACCOUNT THE PROPORTIONALITY CONSTANTS REPRESENTING THE LOSS OF TACTICAL STRENGTH AND THE DECLINE IN PRODUCTIVITY THAT ONE WOULD EXPECT IN AN EVER-CHANGING BATTLE SITUATION. THE MODEL WAS CREATED BY DEVELOPING THIS RELATIONSHIP INTO DIFFERENTIAL EQUATIONS AND INCORPORATING THEIR EQUILIBRIUM CONDITIONS INTO GAME THEORY.

TACTICAL STRENGTH OF ARMY M

PORTION OF FIGHTING STRENGTH DEPLOYED AS A DEFENSE AGAINST ENEMY ATTACKS, OR IN DIRECT COMBAT ON THE BATTLEFIELD.

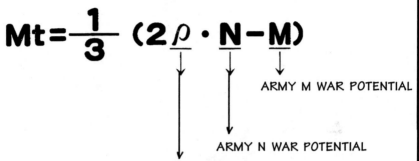

$$Mt = \frac{1}{3}(2\rho \cdot N - M)$$

ARMY M WAR POTENTIAL

ARMY N WAR POTENTIAL

THE LANCHESTER STRATEGY COEFFICIENT
(CUBE ROOT OF THE RATIO OF PRODUCTION RATIO OF THE TWO SIDES)

STRATEGIC STRENGTH OF ARMY M

PORTION OF WAR POTENTIAL DEPLOYED TO ATTACK THE ENEMY'S PRODUCTION / SUPPLY STRENGTH

$$Ms = \frac{2}{3}(2M - \rho \cdot N) = 2\rho Nt$$

| ARMY M WAR POTENTIAL | ARMY N WAR POTENTIAL | ARMY N TACTICAL STRENGTH |

$$M = Mt + Ms$$

ARMY M WAR POTENTIAL – ARMY M TACTICAL STRENGTH + ARMY M STRATEGIC STRENGTH

$$N = Nt + Ns$$

ARMY M WAR POTENTIAL = ARMY N TACTICAL STRENGTH + ARMY N STRATEGIC STRENGTH

MARKET SHARE TARGETS

MAXIMUM TARGET = 73.9 %

EQUILIBRIUM / STABLE TARGET = 41.7 %

MINIMUM TARGET = 26.1 %

IN TERMS OF MARKET SHARE, THIS IS CALLED A "MONOPOLISTIC OLIGOPOLY" THE LEADER HAS A TOTALLY SAFE MONOPOLY POSITION

NO. 1 73.9%

BUT .... A COMPANY CAN BOAST ABSOLUTE STABILITY ONLY WHEN

ITS SHARE IS AT LEAST 73.9 %

A COMPANY MAY HAVE A MONOPOLY SIMPLY BECAUSE THERE IS NO COMPETITION, BUT, IT IS NOT NECESSARILY INVULNERABLE

THE AIM OF THE ORIGINAL LANCHESTER STRATEGY WAS TO INCREASE MARKET SHARE AS MUCH AS POSSIBLE

1 IT IS NOT EASY TO STIMULATE DEMAND

SUNTORY HAS A MONOPOLY IN THE WHISKEY INDUSTRY WITH A MARKET SHARE OF 70%

TOYOTA HAS 44% OF THE AUTOMOBILE MARKET (EXCLUDING COMPACT CARS)

NATIONAL HAS ABOUT 25% OF THE HOUSEHOLD APPLIANCE MARKET . . . .

SO, YOU SEE, EACH FIRM IS IN A DIFFERENT COMPETITIVE SITUATION

SUNTORY BOASTED A 77.5% MARKET SHARE IN 1979
(SOURCE: NIKKEI SANGYO SHINBUN NEWSPAPER)

2 YOU END UP COMPETING WITH OTHER INDUSTRIES

3 THE CORRELATION WITH PROFIT DISAPPEARS

THERE IS A STRONG CORRELATION BETWEEN MARKET SHARE AND PROFIT WITHIN THE RANGE OF 10 % - 74 %

IF YOU RAISE MARKET SHARE TO BETWEEN 10 % AND 74 %, YOUR PROFITS WILL RISE AS WELL

IN THE BEER INDUSTRY, KIRIN IS NO. 1 WITH 62 % AND SAPPORO IS NO. 2 WITH 20 % MARKET SHARE

BUT KIRIN HAS THREE TIMES THE GROSS SALES AND SIX TIMES THE ORDINARY PROFIT OF SAPPORO

HOLY COW ! ! THAT'S A SIGNIFICANT DIFFERENCE ISN'T IT ?

A LARGE SHARE REALLY GIVES YOU AN EDGE

THE SAME APPLIES TO THE BATTLE OVER CUSTOMERS

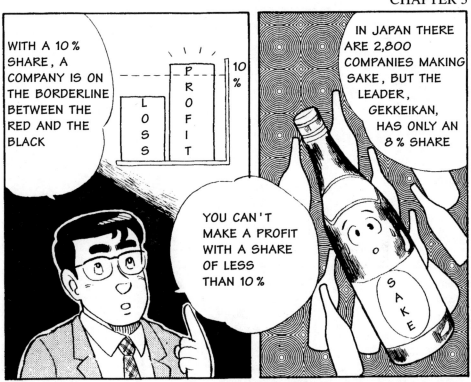

WITH A 10 % SHARE, A COMPANY IS ON THE BORDERLINE BETWEEN THE RED AND THE BLACK

L O S S   P R O F I T   10 %

YOU CAN'T MAKE A PROFIT WITH A SHARE OF LESS THAN 10 %

IN JAPAN THERE ARE 2,800 COMPANIES MAKING SAKE, BUT THE LEADER, GEKKEIKAN, HAS ONLY AN 8 % SHARE

SAKE

SOME COMPANIES AND BRANDS HAVE A 10 % OR HIGHER SHARE IN SOME REGIONS, BUT ONLY A FEW ARE MAKING A PROFIT

PROFIT

EITHER THEY'RE MAKING MORE PROFIT IN OTHER LINES OF BUSINESS, OR THEY'RE LIVING ON THEIR ASSETS

IT'S TOUGH !

NEED A PART TIME JOB

IT IS NOT ENOUGH TO MERELY MAINTAIN A HIGH MARKET SHARE

I GUESS YOU'RE RIGHT

MR. SAKAMOTO'S GROUP GOT US A 75% MARKET SHARE

. . .BUT I COULDN'T BEAR OUR RIVALS' HAVING 25%, AND ORDERED HIM TO RAISE OUR SHARE . . .

. . . OUR SHARE INCREASED SLIGHTLY, BUT OUR PROFITS DIDN'T

YES, I HEARD ABOUT A COMPANY WITH A 77% SHARE WHOSE PROFITS ACTUALLY DECREASED

81

FOR EXAMPLE . .
CASIO HAS BEEN NO. 1
EVER SINCE IT BROKE
THROUGH THE 40%
BARRIER BACK IN 1978.
EXCEPT FOR ONE YEAR,
THEIR MARKET
SHARE HAS ALSO
INCREASED

THIS IS THE
BORDER LINE FOR
PROFITABILITY.
IT IS COMMONLY
REFERRED TO
AS THE 40%

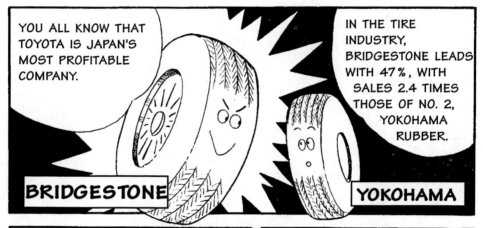

YOU ALL KNOW THAT
TOYOTA IS JAPAN'S
MOST PROFITABLE
COMPANY.

IN THE TIRE
INDUSTRY,
BRIDGESTONE LEADS
WITH 47%, WITH
SALES 2.4 TIMES
THOSE OF NO. 2,
YOKOHAMA
RUBBER.

BRIDGESTONE

YOKOHAMA

BRIDGESTONE'S
PROFITS ARE
FOURTEEN TIMES
THOSE OF
YOKOHAMA
RUBBER

IS THAT
RIGHT ? . .

I DIDN'T
KNOW
THAT ! !

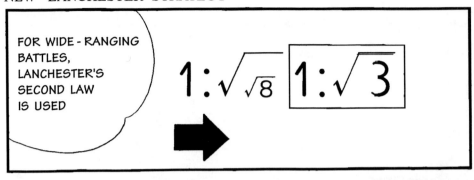

FOR WIDE - RANGING BATTLES, LANCHESTER'S SECOND LAW IS USED

$$1 : \sqrt{\sqrt{8}} \quad \boxed{1 : \sqrt{3}}$$

$$\sqrt{\sqrt{8}} \approx \sqrt{3}$$

$$\sqrt{8} \approx 2.83 \approx 3$$

IN MARKETING WE USE THESE APPROXIMATIONS

LOCAL BATTLES OR SINGLE COMBAT

IN LOCAL BATTLES OR SINGLE COMBAT, THE SHOOTING RANGE IS A THREEFOLD MARGIN

SINCE BATTLES FOR INDIVIDUAL CUSTOMERS ARE LOCAL BATTLES, A THREEFOLD MARGIN PUTS A COMPANY IN AN IRREVERSIBLE POSITION. THE SAME

. . HOLDS FOR A BATTLE BETWEEN TWO COMPANIES. IF YOU HAVE LESS THAN A THREEFOLD MARGIN, YOUR POSITION CAN BE REVERSED

IN 1993, A U.S. TASK FORCE INVADED THE ISLAND OF GRENADA. THE FIRST LANDING OF 20,000 U.S. MILITARY PERSONNEL FACED 17,000 GRENADINO SOLDIERS. HOWEVER, IN SUBSEQUENT LANDINGS, THE NUMBER OF U.S. TROOPS INCREASED TO A TOTAL OF 56,000, FOR A RATIO OF 3:1.

COMPANY MARKET SHARE PERCENTAGE						
	A	**B**	**C**	**D**	**E**	**F**
S C E N A R I O	CASE NO. 1	75% X 3 IRREVERSIBLE	25%				
	CASE NO. 2	60% REVERSIBLE	X 4 IRREVERSIBLE 25% REVERSIBLE	15%			
	CASE NO. 3	50% X 3.3 IRREVERSIBLE	15%	10% REVERSIBLE	10%	REVERSIBLE 10% REVERSIBLE	5%

THE CHART SHOWS SOME POSSIBLE SCENARIOS

I DIDN'T THINK WE COULD GET A LARGER SHARE OF THE ELAWA CO'S BUSINESS, WE'RE CURRENTLY NUMBER 2.

BUT NOW I THINK WE MIGHT BE ABLE TO DO IT

OUR SHARE OF THE MIURA COMPANY'S BUSINESS IS SECURE

MAYBE WE SHOULD SPEND LESS TIME THERE, AND FOCUS ON OTHER CUSTOMERS

SEIBU (LIONS) RESULTS OF SEPTEMBER 3, 1985

BUFFALOS	BRAVES	ORIONS	FIGHTERS	HAWKS
11 — 7	9 — 10	15 — 5	15 — 6	15 — 5

THE BATTLE IS FOUGHT AMONG SIX TEAMS, IN A SINGLE COMBAT, THUS THE 3:1 RATIO

3:1 REFERS TO THE NUMBER OF WINS AND LOSSES. THE LIONS BEAT TWO OTHER TEAMS 3:1

SAY YOUR TARGET IS 41.7%, IF YOU SEGMENT JAPAN INTO 100 REGIONS, ROUNDING DOWN TO 40%

AND IF YOU LEAD IN 40 REGIONS, THERE'S A GOOD CHANCE YOU'LL BECOME THE NATIONAL LEADER.

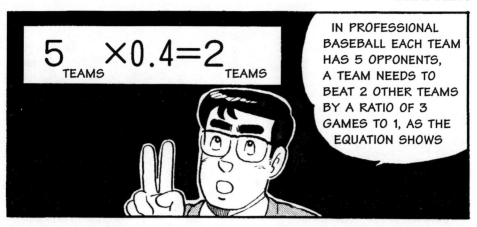

IN PROFESSIONAL BASEBALL EACH TEAM HAS 5 OPPONENTS, A TEAM NEEDS TO BEAT 2 OTHER TEAMS BY A RATIO OF 3 GAMES TO 1, AS THE EQUATION SHOWS

$$5 \text{ TEAMS} \times 0.4 = 2 \text{ TEAMS}$$

SEIBU (LIONS) RESULTS AS OF SEPTEMBER 3, 1986

BUFFALOS	BRAVES	ORIONS	FIGHTERS	HAWKS
14 — 4	14 — 6	18 — 4	12 — 8	9 — 8

IN 1984, THE LIONS LOST THE CHAMPIONSHIP, BUT IN 1983, THEY DEFEATED 2 TEAMS BY A RATIO OF 3:1

THE TIGERS DEFEATED SEVERAL TEAMS BY CLOSE TO A RATIO OF 3:1

HANSHIN (TIGERS) RESULTS AS OF SEPTEMBER 12, 1986

CARPS	GIANTS	DRAGONS	SWALLOWS	WHALES
9 — 13	8 — 12	14 — 5	13 — 5	15 — 5

WELL CHIEF ? WHAT DO YOU THINK OF THAT ? ?

WELL, WELL THIS IS AN INTERESTING ANALOGY

ALL BATTLES HAVE ASPECTS IN COMMON

THE TIGERS' 1986 VICTORY WASN'T AN ACCIDENT

IF WE APPROACH IT FROM THIS VIEWPOINT, PRO BASEBALL SHOULD BE 50 % MORE FUN.

WIDE-RANGING AND STOCHASTIC BATTLES

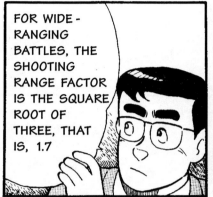

FOR WIDE-RANGING BATTLES, THE SHOOTING RANGE FACTOR IS THE SQUARE ROOT OF THREE, THAT IS, 1.7

IN INDUSTRY-WIDE BATTLES FOR REGIONS OR . . .

IN SECTORS, WHEN THE MARGIN IS MORE THAN A FACTOR OF 1.7 REVERSALS ARE IMPOSSIBLE

ON THE OTHER HAND, WHEN THE MARGIN IS LESS THAN A FACTOR OF 1.7

REVERSALS ARE POSSIBLE. LOOK AT THESE CHARTS

INDUSTRIES WHERE REVERSALS MAY OCCUR

AIR CONDITIONERS
MICROWAVE OVENS
ALUMINUM SIDING
CAUSTIC SODA
COOKING OIL
ETHYLENE
PASSENGER CARS
SHEET GLASS
WRIST WATCHES

INDUSTRIES WHERE REVERSALS ARE UNLIKELY

COLOR FILM
INNER TUBES
FORKLIFTS
TOOTHPASTE
BEER
WHISKEY

SO, YOU ARE SAYING THAT WITH ENOUGH EFFORT, OUR COMPANY CAN BE NO. 1 ?

EXACTLY WHAT DO WE NEED TO DO ?

CALM DOWN, YOU HAVE TO UNDERSTAND THE BASICS FIRST.

BASED ON THE TARGETS AND SHOOTING RANGE, THERE ARE 5 MARKET SHARE PATTERNS

1 POLYOPOLY MARKET

EXAMPLE: 20%, 18%, 16%, 14%, 12%, 10%, 10% MARKET SHARE.

LEADER HAS LESS THAN 26%

EACH COMPANY IS WITHIN A FACTOR OF $\sqrt{3}$ OF NEAREST COMPETITOR

STRONG POSSIBILITY OF SHIFTS IN RANKING

GASOLINE TV A/C SPORTS WEAR

TISSUES ICE CREAM PRE-FAB CEMENT

2 OLIGOPOLY MARKET

EXAMPLE: 30%, 25%, 20%, 11%, 8%, 6% MARKET SHARE

COMBINED SHARE FOR NO.1, NO. 2, AND NO. 3 IS MORE THAN 73.9%

NO. 2 AND NO. 3 TOGETHER HAVE A LARGER SHARE THAN NO. 1

A THREE - WAY BATTLE

WRIST WATCHES MOTOR SCOOTERS

3 DUOPOLY MARKET

EXAMPLE: 38%, 36%, 18%, 5%, 3% MARKET SHARE

COMBINED SHARE FOR NO. 1 AND NO. 2 EXCEEDS 73.9%;

NO. 1 AND NO. 2 ARE WITHIN A FACTOR OF $\sqrt{3}$. LAW NO. 1

APPLIES TO THIS BATTLE, THE SECOND-PLACE FIRM IS NOT

IN AN OVERLY DISADVANTAGEOUS POSITION.

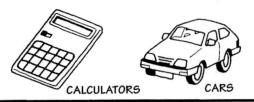

CALCULATORS CARS DETERGENT

4 PREMIUM MARKET

EXAMPLE : 43 %, 24 %, 17 %, 9 %, 7 % MARKET SHARE
LEADER HAS MORE THAN 41.7 % (EQUILIBRIUM TARGET).
LEADER IS MORE THAN A FACTOR OF $\sqrt{3}$ AHEAD OF
SECOND PLACE.
LEADER IS FAR AHEAD OF THE COMPETITION.

5 MONOPOLY MARKET

EXAMPLE : 74 %, 16 %, 7 %, 3 % MARKET SHARE

THE NUMBER ONE COMPANY HAS MORE THAN 73.9 %
THE BATTLE HAS ARRIVED AT ITS CONCLUSION

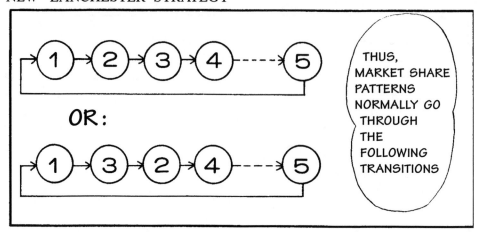

THUS, MARKET SHARE PATTERNS NORMALLY GO THROUGH THE FOLLOWING TRANSITIONS

THREE COMPANIES MAY BREAK AWAY FROM A POLYOPOLY MARKET. A THREE-WAY BATTLE WILL PRODUCE TWO WINNERS, WHO WILL VIE FOR FIRST PLACE. THE SOLE WINNER'S ADVANTAGE WILL CONTINUE TO INCREASE.

OR TWO COMPANIES MAY BREAK AWAY FROM A POLYOPOLY MARKET. ANOTHER COMPANY MAY MAKE A COMEBACK, RESULTING IN A THREE-WAY BATTLE. THE VICTOR WILL CONTINUE TO SURGE AHEAD.

BUT IF THE LEADER'S SHARE GROWS TOO LARGE, IT RISKS MERGERS OR TIE-UPS, MANDATED BREAKUP, LOSS OF EXCLUSIVITY OF PATENTS, NOT TO MENTION TECHNOLOGICAL INNOVATIONS, WHICH MAY PUT IT BACK INTO THE POLYOPOLY POSITION.

GENTLEMEN, THAT'S HOW THE STORY GOES

HAVE YOU BEEN FOLLOWING ME?

MARKET SHARE PATTERN

SO, IN OUR BUSINESS, THERE'S PLENTY OF ROOM FOR REVERSALS

YES, WE MIGHT JUST BE ABLE TO DO IT USING THIS STRATEGY

I'M GLAD YOU'RE ALL IN AGREEMENT ON THIS

SINCE THE LEADER HAS 34%, AND WE HAVE 27%, WE'RE DEFINITELY WITHIN SHOOTING RANGE

SUMMARY

Research on Lanchester's first and second laws was done during World War II by a U.S. Navy Operations Research team. The team included a Columbia University mathematics professor, Bernard O. Koopman, who had been drafted into the Navy.

The researchers, mindful that the supply of troops and weapons, the training of troops, and the production of weapons are important considerations during a prolonged battle, created the Lanchester strategy model.

We will describe the Lanchester strategy model later. First, we will describe the market share targets and the shooting range theory drawn from the model.

Market Share Targets

The term market share describes the percentage of the total market for a specific product held by the company or companies under discussion. The following three targets have been derived from the Lanchester strategy model.

Maximum Target (73.9%)

This is called a "monopoly share." The leader is in a position of absolute stability and dominance. The original Lanchester strategy advocates raising market share to the highest level possible. However, the New Lanchester Strategy sets the upper limit at 73.9%, and advises against acquiring a share larger than that.

When a company's market share becomes too large,

1. It becomes difficult to stimulate demand.

2. The leader comes into competition with other industries or specialties.

3. The correlation between market share and profitability disappears.

Equilibrium or Stable Target (41.7%)

When a company's goal is to dominate its competitors, its target becomes the acquisition of a share consisting of more than half the market, i.e., more than 50%. However, the Lanchester strategy model produces the figure of 41.7% as the share necessary to dominate a market. When three or more companies are competing for the lead, one of them becomes the industry leader, and also establishes itself in a dominant position, by acquiring a market share of at least 41.7%. In addition, the gap in profitability between the leader and its rivals widens when the leader's market share exceeds 41.7%. This target is usually rounded to 40%.

Minimum Target (26.1%)

A company can be a market leader, and still be in an unstable position, i.e., in danger of having its position reversed. The boundary between stability and instability is 26.1%.

Once a company has exceeded this borderline figure of 26.1%, it begins to stand above the crowd. The profitability factor also changes at this point, as it does with the 41.7% target.

The above-mentioned three targets should be used to

1. Ascertain a company's position as far as market share is concerned

2. Set market share targets for the future

Furthermore, these targets can be applied to a company's share of a client's business. However, since it is difficult to acquire an accurate grasp of a company's share in a specific region or its share of a particular client's business, it ultimately becomes necessary to do an extensive market survey.

The Shooting Range Theory

According to the Lanchester strategy model, in a battle of the single combat type or a local battle between two companies, if one company's war potential exceeds its opponent's war potential by more than a factor of three or, in a wide-ranging, comprehensive battle, exceeds its opponent's fighting strength by a factor of √ 3, it becomes undefeatable. This is known as the shooting range theory.

In a two-company battle or a battle for individual customers, the company with a margin of a factor of three or, in regional or market area battles, the company with a margin of a factor of √ 3, is in an irreversible position. Conversely, companies with margins narrower than either of these may see their positions reversed.

The shooting range theory can be applied to competitions between first place and third place, and competitions between second and third place, as well as to battles between companies in first and second place.

Applying the Lanchester Strategy Model to Marketing

War potential is a combination of tactical and strategic strength. Tactical strength is the fighting strength demonstrated in defending against enemy attacks and directly on the battlefield. Strategic strength is the potential to attack and destroy the enemy's production and supply strength. The correspondence between the two is shown in the chart below. Mutual war potential corresponds as a whole, but strategic strength corresponds to the enemy's production and supply strength, while tactical strength corresponds to the enemy's tactical and strategic strength.

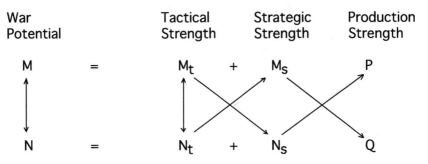

War Potential		Tactical Strength		Strategic Strength		Production Strength
M	=	M_t	+	M_s		P
N	=	N_t	+	N_s		Q

Lanchester Strategy Model Equations

$$M_t = \frac{1}{3}(2\rho \cdot N - M)$$

$$M_s = \frac{2}{3}(2M - \rho N) = 2\rho N_t$$

Where ρ is the Lanchester strategy coefficient, representing the cube root of the ratio of production on the two sides ($\sqrt[3]{(P/Q)}$).

Lanchester's Equilibrium Conditions

The conditions for equilibrium between Army M and Army N are shown below.

First equilibrium condition: $\frac{\rho}{2}N < M < 2\rho N$ or $\frac{1}{2\rho}M < N < \frac{2}{\rho}M$

Second equilibrium condition: $M_t < \frac{2}{3}M$, $N_t < \frac{2}{3}N$

Stable or Equilibrium Target (41.7%)

If one company is to dominate over the competition, it must have war potential consisting of a larger amount of indirect competitiveness (Ms) than direct competitiveness (Mt). If we expand this concept in accordance with the Lanchester Strategy model, we arrive at 41.7%, as shown below.

$$M_s > M_t$$

$$2(2M - \rho N) > 1(2\rho N - M)$$

$$4M - 2\rho N > 2\rho N - M$$

$$\frac{M}{N} > \frac{4\rho}{5}$$

$$\frac{M}{N} > \frac{4}{5} \sqrt[3]{\frac{P}{Q}}$$

$$\left[\frac{M}{N}\right]^3 > \frac{64}{125} \cdot \frac{P}{Q}$$

In a competitive situation, $\frac{M}{N} \approx \frac{P}{Q}$ approximately

$$\left[\frac{M}{N}\right]^2 > \frac{64}{125}$$

$$\frac{M}{N} > \frac{8}{\sqrt{125}}$$

Here, M and N represent market share. M represents the leader's share and N the competition. Therefore, N + M = 1.

$$\frac{M}{N} > \frac{8}{\sqrt{125}}$$

$$M\sqrt{125} > 8 - 8M$$

$$(8 + \sqrt{125}) > 8$$

$$M > \frac{8}{8 + \sqrt{125}} = \frac{8}{19.1803}$$

$$M > 0.4171$$

Minimum Target (26.1%)

When the leader's market share exceeds 41.7%, that company has achieved an overwhelming edge over the rest of the competition. However, in some cases, the leader cannot battle all the competition.

Since the leader's market competitiveness cannot match the competitiveness of all its rivals, it falls beneath the lower limit of Lanchester's first equilibrium condition.

$$M < \frac{\rho}{2} N$$

$$\frac{M}{N} < \frac{1}{2}\rho$$

$$\frac{M}{N} < \frac{1}{2}\sqrt[3]{\frac{P}{Q}}$$

In a competitive situation, $\quad \frac{M}{N} \approx \frac{P}{Q} \quad$ approximately

$$\frac{M}{N} < \frac{1}{2}\sqrt[3]{\frac{M}{N}}$$

$$\left[\frac{M}{N}\right]^3 < \frac{1}{8}\cdot\frac{M}{N}$$

$$\left[\frac{M}{N}\right]^2 < \frac{1}{8}$$

$$\frac{M}{N} < \frac{1}{\sqrt{8}}$$

Here, M and N represent market share, M represents the leader's share, and N the competitor's share. Therefore, N + M = 1.

$$\frac{M}{1-M} < \frac{1}{\sqrt{8}}$$

$$M\sqrt{8} < 1-M$$

$$(1+\sqrt{8})M < 1$$

$$M < \frac{1}{1+\sqrt{8}}$$

$$M < 0.2612$$

Maximum Target (73.9%)

When a company is the market leader, and it has an overwhelming edge over the competition, that company has acquired a secure, absolute monopoly. Since the leader is more competitive than all the competition combined, the upper limit of Lanchester's first equilibrium condition has been exceeded.

$$2\rho N < M$$

$$2\rho < \frac{M}{N}$$

$$2\sqrt[3]{\frac{P}{Q}} < \frac{M}{N}$$

In a competitive situation, $\frac{M}{N} \approx \frac{P}{Q}$ approximately

$$2\sqrt[3]{\frac{M}{N}} < \frac{M}{N}$$

$$8\,\frac{M}{N} < \left[\frac{M}{N}\right]^3$$

$$8 < \left[\frac{M}{N}\right]^2$$

$$\sqrt{8} < \frac{M}{N}$$

Here, M and N represent market share, M represents the leader's share, and N the competition's share. Therefore, M + N = 1.

$$\sqrt{8} < \frac{M}{1-M}$$

$$\sqrt{8} - M\sqrt{8} < M$$

$$\sqrt{8} < (1 + \sqrt{8})M$$

$$\frac{\sqrt{8}}{1 + \sqrt{8}} < M$$

$$0.7388 < M$$

Shooting Range

Minimum Target $\quad M < \dfrac{1}{1 + \sqrt{8}} \quad$ (M < 0.2612)

Maximum Target $\quad \dfrac{\sqrt{8}}{1 + \sqrt{8}} < M \quad$ (0.7388 < M)

NEW LANCHESTER STRATEGY

Companies with a market share below the lower-limit target will be ignored by other companies, while those which hold a share larger than the upper limit target ignore other companies. This means that the cannons fired by an army ranking below the minimum target cannot reach an opponent ranking above the maximum target. Since we may assume that the former army is outside shooting range, shooting range is equal to √8, as shown above.

When the ratio of market share between two specific companies is greater than √8, they are not within shooting range of each other. The lower ranking company will have difficulty engineering a reversal.

Conversely, when a company acquires a share that is at least √8 times that of its competitor, its position is secure. Since the competitive situation changes by the second, there is no point in being overly precise, 3 may be substituted for √8 (2.8284).

However, √8 is applied to the single-combat type of battle, and for a wide-ranging battle, Lanchester's second law is applied. Therefore, the figures used to represent the competitiveness of the opposing forces are squared. Since the squared ratio is 1: √8, the original competitiveness ratio is 1:√√8.

As before, there is no need to be overly precise. Therefore, √3 ≈ 1.7 may be substituted for 1: √√8 (1.6818).

CHAPTER FOUR

THE THREE PRINCIPLES OF THE
NEW LANCHESTER STRATEGY

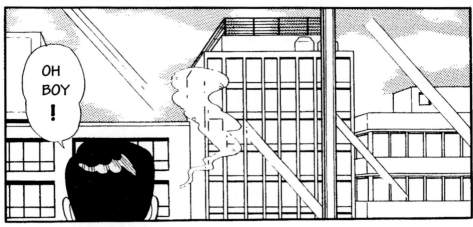

THE MANAGER IS THE ONLY ONE ON MY SIDE

WHAT ABOUT THE DIRECTOR?

I CAN'T LET IT BOTHER ME. I MUST PRESENT MY CASE WITH CONFIDENCE

MR. SAKAMOTO

HERE IS FRESH COFFEE !

I KNOW ITS TOUGH . . .

BUT . . . HANG IN THERE

OH . . .

WELL THANK YOU

OKAY... NOW I WILL EXPLAIN THE THREE PRINCIPLES OF THE NEW LANCHESTER STRATEGY

THE NEW LANCHESTER STRATEGY IS BASED ON THE ORIGINAL LANCHESTER STRATEGY

....SO, IT MAY BE PRESUMPTUOUS TO ADD THE WORD "NEW"

1   THE NO. 1 PRINCIPLE

THE ORIGINAL LANCHESTER STRATEGY ALSO HAS A NO. 1 PRINCIPLE WHICH IS SIMPLY A MATTER OF BECOMING THE LEADER

HOWEVER, IN THE NEW LANCHESTER STRATEGY,

THE NO. 1 PRINCIPLE MEANS ACQUIRING AN OVERWHELMING LEAD

NO.1 PRINCIPLE

IN THE NEW STRATEGY, WE HAVE THE SHOOTING RANGE CONCEPT

WHEN THE NO. 2 COMPANY BEGINS TO CATCH UP WITH THE LEADER

THE LEADER MAY LOOSE ITS NO. 1 POSITION

IF THE LEADER HAS 40%, AND NO. 2 26%, THE LEADER DOESN'T HAVE THAT MUCH OF AN ADVANTAGE

IN A BATTLE, EVERYTHING IS RELATIVE. IT'S THE DISTANCE BETWEEN THE TWO SIDES THAT MATTERS.

TO SUM UP . .

THE NO. 1 PRINCIPLE TELLS US TO BE FIRST IN AS MANY WAYS AS POSSIBLE

ON THE NEXT PAGE, WE'LL SEE THE DIFFERENT WAYS OF BEING NO. 1

TYPES AND CLASSES OF NO. 1

NO. 1 PRODUCT

A PRODUCT THAT COMMANDS A SHARE
HIGHER THAN THAT HELD BY NO. 2 BY A
FACTOR OF $\sqrt{3}$ (AMONG PRODUCTS THAT
HAVE BEEN SUBDIVIDED INTO GROUPS)
IN THE ENTIRE PRODUCT MARKET.

NO. 1 REGION

A REGION IN WHICH YOUR COMPANY
COMMANDS A SHARE HIGHER THAN THAT
HELD BY THE NO. 2 BY A FACTOR OF $\sqrt{3}$
(AMONG SEGMENTED REGIONS OR AFTER
REGIONAL SEGMENTATION).

NO. 1 IN CUSTOMER BASE

A CUSTOMER BASE IN WHICH YOUR COMPANY
COMMANDS A SHARE HIGHER THAN NO. 2 BY
A FACTOR OF $\sqrt{3}$ (AFTER SEGMENTATION BY
INDUSTRY, PROFESSION, AGE OR CHANNEL).

NO. 1 WITH CUSTOMER

A CUSTOMER OF WHOSE BUSINESS YOUR
COMPANY BOASTS A SHARE MORE THAN
THREE TIMES THAT OF THE NO. 2.

NO. 1 WITH AGENCY

AN AGENCY IN WHICH YOUR COMPANY HOLDS
A SHARE THREE TIMES THAT OF THE NO. 2.

THE NO. 1 PRINCIPLE IN TERMS OF THE
THE ORIGINAL LANCHESTER STRATEGY

STRATEGY OF THE STRONG	STRATEGY OF THE WEAK
NO.1	NO.1
NO.1 IN REGION	NO.1 PRODUCT
⬆	⬆
NO.1 WITH AGENCY OR CUSTOMER	NO.1 WITH AGENCY OR CUSTOMER
⬆	⬆
NO.1 PRODUCT	NO.1 IN REGION

THE ORIGINAL LANCHESTER STRATEGY MENTIONS THREE TYPES OF NO. 1: PRODUCTS, AGENCIES AND REGIONS

THE IDEA WAS THAT THE STRONG (NO.1 FIRM) SHOULD BEGIN BY CREATING A NO.1 PRODUCT, AND THE WEAK BY BECOMING NO.1 IN A REGION

ALSO, THE STRATEGY FOR CREATING A NO. 1 PRODUCT OR REGION WASN'T CLEARLY STATED

AGENCIES WERE DEFINED AS CUSTOMERS. AS A RESULT, INTERPRETATIONS VARIED

NO. 1 PRINCIPLE OF THE NEW LANCHESTER STRATEGY

WHERE NO. 1 OUTDISTANCES NO. 2 BY MORE THAN THE SHOOTING RANGE

NO.1 STRATEGY OF THE STRONG

1. CREATE AS MANY NO.1 PRODUCTS AS POSSIBLE
2. THEN MAKE ALL PRODUCTS HANDLED NO.1 PRODUCTS

(THIS IS HOW A MANUFACTURER CREATES A NO.1 AGENCY)

NO.1 STRATEGY OF THE WEAK

1. AQUIRE A NO.1 CUSTOMER WITHIN A LIMITED GEOGRAPHIC AREA
2. CREATE AS MANY NO.1 CUSTOMER BASES AND DISTRICTS AS POSSIBLE
3. BECOME NO.1 IN A TERRITORY OR A PRODUCT MARKET

No. 1 AGENCY

No. 1 PRODUCTS

No. 1 PRODUCT

No. 1 REGION

No. 1 CUSTOMER BASE

No. 1 DISTRICT

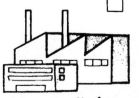

No. 1 CUSTOMER

118

2 ATTACK THE WEAK, AND WEAK POINTS

A KEY PHRASE FROM THE LANCHESTER STRATEGY IS "SEPARATE COMPETITIVE TARGETS AND OFFENSIVE TARGETS"

RIVAL TARGETS

OFFENSIVE TARGET

THE WEAK SHOULD GO TO BATTLE AGAINST WEAKER RIVALS, RATHER THAN TRYING TO COMPETE WITH THE STRONG

THE GOAL OF THE WEAK SHOULD BE TO RAISE MARKET SHARE BY DEFEATING WEAKER RIVALS, AND THEN TO ENGAGE IN SINGLE COMBAT WITH THE STRONG

THUS, THE COMPETITIVE TARGET IS A RIVAL WITH AN EQUAL MARKET SHARE OR ONE NOTCH ABOVE YOU

THE OFFENSIVE TARGET IS A RIVAL COMPANY ONE NOTCH BELOW YOUR COMPANY IN MARKET SHARE

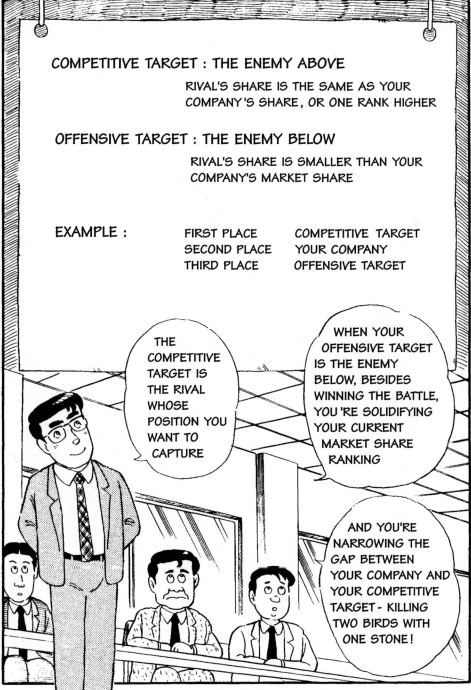

COMPETITIVE TARGET : THE ENEMY ABOVE

RIVAL'S SHARE IS THE SAME AS YOUR
COMPANY'S SHARE, OR ONE RANK HIGHER

OFFENSIVE TARGET : THE ENEMY BELOW

RIVAL'S SHARE IS SMALLER THAN YOUR
COMPANY'S MARKET SHARE

EXAMPLE :
FIRST PLACE   COMPETITIVE TARGET
SECOND PLACE   YOUR COMPANY
THIRD PLACE   OFFENSIVE TARGET

THE COMPETITIVE TARGET IS THE RIVAL WHOSE POSITION YOU WANT TO CAPTURE

WHEN YOUR OFFENSIVE TARGET IS THE ENEMY BELOW, BESIDES WINNING THE BATTLE, YOU'RE SOLIDIFYING YOUR CURRENT MARKET SHARE RANKING

AND YOU'RE NARROWING THE GAP BETWEEN YOUR COMPANY AND YOUR COMPETITIVE TARGET - KILLING TWO BIRDS WITH ONE STONE!

THAT MAKES SENSE, BUT IT SEEMS CRUEL TO ATTACK AN UNDERDOG

REMEMBER, BOTH BASEBALL TEAMS, THE LIONS AND THE TIGERS, ATTACKED WEAKER TEAMS MERCILESSLY

I UNDERSTAND HOW YOU FEEL, BUT THIS IS THE AGE OF SURVIVAL

WE CAN'T AFFORD TO BE SO EASY GOING

I USED TO FEEL THE SAME WAY, BUT IF WE GET TOO SENTIMENTAL

WE'LL BE THE ONES WHO WILL LOSE OUT. IF WE DON'T GET THEM FIRST, THEY'LL GET US

BUT EVEN IF WE USE THIS STRATEGY, NO. 1 IS GOING TO BE ATTACKING US

THAT'S CERTAINLY A POSSIBILITY

FOR THE MARKET LEADER, THE COMPETITIVE AND OFFENSIVE TARGETS ARE THE SAME.

IF WE'RE NO. 2, WE EXPECT THE NO. 1 RANKING COMPANY TO BE COMING AFTER US.

WHAT DO WE DO IN A CASE LIKE THAT?

WHEN YOU'RE BATTLING WITH YOUR OFFENSIVE TARGET, YOU HAVE TO GIVE EVERYTHING YOU'VE GOT

BUT, IN REAL LIFE THERE ARE MANY BATTLE SCENARIOS. YOU DON'T ALWAYS GET THE RESULTS YOU EXPECT.

I'LL DISCUSS THIS MORE LATER, BUT THE POINT IS THAT YOU'RE COMPETITIVE IF YOUR COMPANY HAS SOMETHING THAT YOUR RIVALS DON'T

LET ME ADD THAT THE NEW LANCHESTER STRATEGY TELLS US TO AIM FOR THE ENEMY'S WEAK POINT

BULLYING THE WEAK ACCORDING TO THE TRADITIONAL LANCHESTER STRATEGY:
ATTACK THE ENEMY BELOW

ATTACKS ON THE WEAK AND WEAK POINTS ACCORDING TO THE NEW LANCHESTER STRATEGY:
* ATTACK THE ENEMY BELOW
* ATTACK RIVAL'S WEAK POINTS

3 PRINCIPLE OF ONE - POINT CONCENTRATION

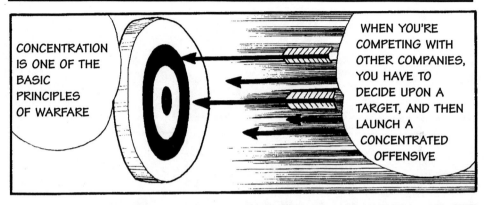

CONCENTRATION IS ONE OF THE BASIC PRINCIPLES OF WARFARE

WHEN YOU'RE COMPETING WITH OTHER COMPANIES, YOU HAVE TO DECIDE UPON A TARGET, AND THEN LAUNCH A CONCENTRATED OFFENSIVE

SINCE THE WEAK HAVE FEWER RESOURCES THAN THE STRONG, THE WEAK MUST CONCENTRATE THEIR STRENGTH ON ONE TARGET

MISERY

MACHINERY COMPANY XY USED TO BE IN FIFTH PLACE

BUT IT FOCUSED ON ONE REGION, LAUNCHED A CONCENTRATED ATTACK, AND AFTER FOUR YEARS BECAME NO. 1 IN THE INDUSTRY

THERE ARE MANY TASKS FOR US TO ACCOMPLISH NOW

BUT IF WE TRY TO DO TOO MUCH WE'LL ONLY GET HALF-BAKED RESULTS

WE NEED TO SET OUR PRIORITIES, AND TACKLE THEM ONE BY ONE

I CAN'T ARGUE WITH THAT. I SEE TWO PROBLEMS HERE

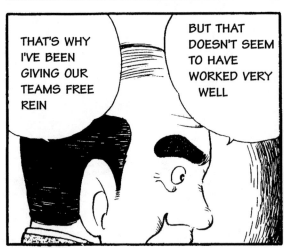

THAT'S WHY I'VE BEEN GIVING OUR TEAMS FREE REIN

BUT THAT DOESN'T SEEM TO HAVE WORKED VERY WELL

129

YOU ALL SEEM TO EMPHASIZE GROWTH AND MARKET SIZE

CONCENTRATION

BUT WE'RE IN THE WEAK CATEGORY SO ACCORDING TO THE NO.1 PRINCIPLE, WE HAVE TO CHOOSE A TARGET

THE ULTIMATE PURPOSE OF ONE-POINT CONCENTRATION IS BECOMING SOME FORM OF NO.1

YES, BUT IF WE CONCENTRATE ON A SMALL MARKET, TOTAL SALES AREN'T GOING TO RISE MUCH, THIS DOESN'T SEEM VERY EFFICIENT

NO, IT'S NOT EFFICIENT, BUT SUCH EFFORTS RESULT IN SUBSTANTIAL GAINS

OUR BIGGEST SHARE WAS IN REGION A, AND THE GAP BETWEEN OUR COMPANY AND THE NO. 1 WAS RATHER NARROW THERE

ARE YOU TALKING ABOUT THAT BASIN REGION?

YES THAT'S RIGHT !

OUR STUDY SHOWED THAT OTHER COMPANIES VISIT THAT REGION ONLY A FEW TIMES A YEAR

WE WERE DOING THE SAME THING THEY WERE

SO, I HAD MY PEOPLE VISIT THERE ONCE A MONTH, AND I ALSO WENT THERE

THE SECOND QUESTION IS THE DEGREE OF CONCENTRATION, MANY PEOPLE THINK THAT ONE-POINT CONCENTRATION MEANS CONCENTRATING ALL ONE'S FORCES

THIS ASPECT OF THE ORIGINAL LANCHESTER STRATEGY HAS NOT BEEN UNDERSTOOD

DUE TO THE RELATIVE NATURE OF BATTLES, YOU MUST GAUGE YOUR CONCENTRATION LEVEL BY YOUR OPPONENT'S

THE EFFORT YOU MUST INVEST MUST BE GREATER THAN THAT OF YOUR COMPETITIVE TARGET

THEY ALL FOCUS ON GROWTH PRODUCTS, GROWTH MARKETS, OR PRODUCTS THAT HAVE A LARGE MARKET SHARE OR ARE BIG SELLERS

SINCE EVERY COMPANY IS MAKING AN EFFORT, IT ISN'T EASY TO INVEST MORE EFFORT THAN YOUR COMPETITIVE TARGET IS.

ONE-POINT CONCENTRATION ACCORDING TO THE ORIGINAL LANCHESTER STRATEGY: INVEST ALL YOUR EFFORT, OR AT LEAST 3 TIMES THAT OF YOUR OPPONENT

ONE-POINT CONCENTRATION ACCORDING TO THE NEW LANCHESTER STRATEGY: RELATIVE INVESTMENT OF EFFORT (INCLUDING THE CUMULATIVE FACTOR) SEE CHAPTER 5 FOR DETAILS

SUMMARY

The three main points of the New Lanchester Strategy are as follows:

1. The No. 1 principle

According to the original Lanchester Strategy, only No. 1, or the leader, boasts an absolute advantage in a battle. The goal is to segment the market, and proceed to become No.1 in as many ways as possible. The new Lanchester strategy also stresses the importance of No. 1, but differs on the following points.

The definition of No. 1

When the original Lanchester Strategy refers to No. 1, it is describing the company in first place, or the market leader. However, there is more than one type of first-place situation. For instance, there may be a wide gap between the leader and No. 2. Conversely, there may be only a narrow margin between the leader and No. 2, and in a situation like this, the leader risks a reversal.

Furthermore, the leader's market share may be 40% or 26%, but the significance of these numbers may change, depending on rivals' market shares. The New Lanchester Strategy introduces the concept of a dominant No. 1. This particular first-place position is more meaningful than first place or a 40% share because, in this case, the leader is out of shooting range, out of the reach of No. 2.

In battle, the relative strength of the two opposing sides is the main determining factor. The same applies to corporate competition — the key factor is difference in market share.

How to create No. 1's

According to the original Lanchester strategy, the goal is to segment regions, clients and products, and strive to create as many No. 1's as possible. The strategy for the weak (second place or lower) is to acquire the number one position in a particular region, then to acquire the majority of a client's business and finally, to create a No. 1 product.

The strategy for the strong (first place) is to focus on a product, a client, and a region, in that order.

However, the original version of the Lanchester strategy is unclear on two points:

1. Are three types of segmentation, i.e., regional, client, and product areas sufficient?

2. Does "client" mean agency, retailer, or end user?

The New Lanchester Strategy segments the No. 1 areas as follows:

No. 1 Product

Products are classified into groups, and a No. 1 product is defined as one that has a share greater than the No. 2 product by a factor of $\sqrt{3}$ in a particular territory or in the entire area in which the product is marketed.

No. 1 in Region

Territories are subdivided, and a No. 1 region is defined as one in which a company holds a share greater than that of No. 2 by a factor of $\sqrt{3}$.

No. 1 in Customer Base

Clients are segmented into categories such as industry, channel, profession. A number one customer base is defined as one in which a company holds a share greater than that of No. 2 by a factor of $\sqrt{3}$.

No. 1 with Client

A client, i.e., a retailer, end user, or consumer of whose business a company possesses a share more than three times that of No. 2.

No. 1 with Agency

Where a manufacturer is concerned, an agency of whose business that manufacturer has three times the share of No. 2 (contractual agency).
Techniques to create various types of No. 1

| Strategy of the Strong | Strategy of the Weak |

#1 in region
↑
#1 with client
↑
#1 in customer base
↑
(#1 with agency)
↑
#1 product
(entire product line)
↑
#1 product

#1 product
#1 with agency
↑
#1 in region
#1 in district
↑
#1 in customer base
↑
#1 with client

In the New Lanchester Strategy, the order in which No. 1's are created has been revised as follows:

Strategy of the Weak

The goal of the weak is to create a No. 1 region. Therefore, the underdog must first pinpoint a region or territory, and within that region, create as many No. 1 clients (particularly major clients) as possible. When that has been accomplished, the next task is to create a No. 1 customer base and a number one region.

By increasing the number of No. 1 regions, the weak can become No. 1 in a sales territory or in an entire marketing area. Then, the underdog will have a No. 1 agency and/or a No. 1 product.

Strategy of the Strong

The strong should focus on one product or several products, and proceed to create a No. 1 product. By having many No. 1 products, they can achieve No. 1 status for their entire product line. (Manufacturers would use this same process to create a number one agency).

The strong can then acquire a No. 1 customer base, a No. 1 customer, and more No. 1 regions.

Priority attacks on the weak and on weak points

When the original Lanchester Strategy addresses "the principle of bullying the weak," what is meant is "separate the competitive target and the offensive target." Since the competitive target is the rival you are currently attempting to reverse, your opponent is one with a market share equal to yours, or one notch above you. An offensive target is a rival company whose share of a customer's business you are attempting to wrest away from it. This opponent is a rival one notch below you or at the bottom of the heap.

Japanese companies tend to be extremely emotional about this subject. They are continually conscious of higher-ranking companies, particularly the market leader. This awareness manifests itself as a sort of complex about the strong. The tendency is particularly pronounced in the No. 2 company, or in one that once held a high market share. Furthermore, when a company with a strong division is developing a strategy to strengthen a weak division, it often forgets about its strong division, and becomes overly conscious of the market leader in the division in which it is weak. However, in a battle that pits the weak against the strong, the weak have no chance of winning. The opponent is a rival with a share equal to yours or in a position one notch above you; the offensive target is a rival whose customers you wish to expropriate and, in this case, is a company one rank below you, or at the bottom of the heap.

Battles are fought to be won. The weak must avoid doing battle with stronger rivals. They must vanquish their weaker rivals and, after a series of such battles, reach a position where they are ready to engage in single combat with the strong.

Since the offensive is always against a weaker rival, this principle is referred to as "the principle of bullying the weak."

The New Lanchester Strategy introduces the concept of "going after your rival's weak points." No matter how strong a company is, its operation cannot be perfect, since it is run by human beings. There are sure to be areas that are not well defended, or weak points.

For instance, even if your rival has a higher share, you should be able to make a breakthrough by attacking blind spots or weak points. The above-mentioned two strategies, i.e., "attacking the enemy below" and "going after your rival's weak points," comprise the "principle of priority attack on the weak and on weak points" in the New Lanchester Strategy.

The Principle of One-Point Concentration

Concentration is a fundamental principle of war. This principle also applies to business competition, where it is necessary to concentrate strength on a selected area or areas, and is called the principle of one-point concentration.

Since the weak have fewer resources than the strong, the weak cannot win if they spread their resources too thinly. Therefore, they must segment regions, products, channels, or customer bases, for instance, and choose which one or ones to focus on.

According to this one-point concentration principle, there are two tasks that must be accomplished.

1. Decide what to concentrate on

As a rule, the strong should choose a product, and the weak a region, just as would be done according to the No. 1 principle. In this case, the strong should focus on market scale or growth possibilities. The weak must choose an area in which they stand a chance of winning, one in which they might possibly dominate. The first goal for the weak is to win, in other words, to create a success story. The main purpose of one-point concentration, after all, is to create No. 1's.

2. Decide how much to concentrate (size of sales force, frequency of sales calls, volume of direct mail, flyers, etc.).

Many companies use "concentration" as a slogan, but continue with their old habits. In that case, of course, nothing is going to change; there will be no reversals. When the amount of effort invested changes, and only then, the situation changes.

The original Lanchester Strategy mentions concentrated attacks, as well as making three times the effort that the enemy makes. However, this point has been misinterpreted, resulting in some companies investing all their resources, which was not the idea. Since battles are decided by the relative strengths of the opposing forces, the level of concentration is determined by the enemy's level of investment. Therefore, the New Lanchester Strategy proposes a degree of concentration (including the cumulative factor) that exceeds that of the opponent, i.e., the competitive target. See Chapter 5 for details.

CHAPTER FIVE

APPLICATIONS TO TACTICAL STRENGTH

145

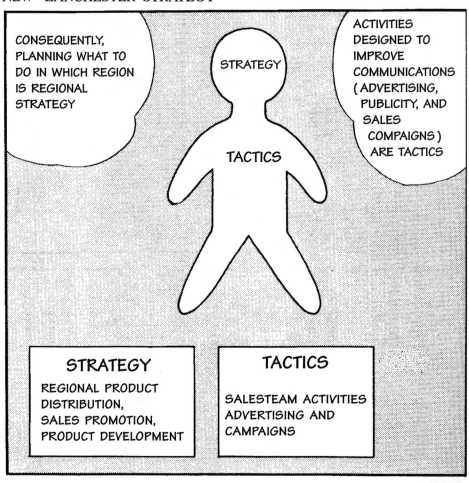

EVALUATIONS OF SALES PERSONNEL HAVE TENDED TO FOCUS ON PERFORMANCE

RESULTS WERE EVERYTHING, THE IDEA THAT IT'S OK TO DO ANYTHING THAT WORKS STILL PERSISTS

THE SAME GOES FOR DIRECT MAIL CAMPAIGNS LAUNCHED BY RETAILERS AND THE SERVICE SECTOR

BUY NOW

NEW NEW NEW

SPECIAL 20% OFF

SALE!

BUT WHEN THE FOCUS IS ON RESULTS, IT'S IMPOSSIBLE TO IMPROVE THEM, OR TO EXPLAIN FAILURES

HUH ?!

YOU NEED A SCIENTIFIC GRASP OF THE PROCESS THAT PRODUCES THE RESULTS

FIRST.... LET'S LOOK AT THE INDIVIDUAL SALESPERSON

HE'S FIGHTING A LOCAL BATTLE, SO LANCHESTER'S FIRST LAW APPLIES

BUT IT'S NOT EASY TO GET A GRASP ON THESE ATTRIBUTES OR TO QUANTIFY THEM

CHARISMA

KNOWLEDGE

SALES TECHNIQUE

THE SALES FORCE OF ANY COMPANY CAN BE DESCRIBED AS
10 % EXCELLENT
80 % AVERAGE
10 % POOR

EXCELLENT

AVERAGE

POOR

YES, AND OUR COMPANY IS NO EXCEPTION I'M AFRAID

I GUESS I'M IN THE "AVERAGE" GROUP

I'M RIGHT UP AT THE TOP !

ON THE NEXT PAGE I'LL SHOW YOU HOW THESE GROUPS ARE MADE

151

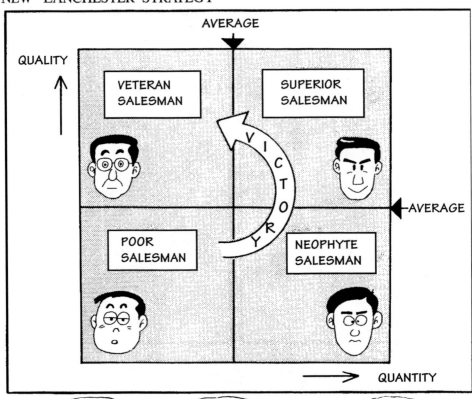

WE SHOULD FIRST THINK ABOUT INCREASING OUR "OFFENSIVE QUANTITY"

IF WE INCREASE OFFENSIVE QUANTITY, QUALITY WILL RISE AUTOMATICALLY

IN JAPAN WE TEND TO FOCUS ON QUALITY . . .

BUT REMEMBER THAT THE SITUATION BECOMES UNMANAGEABLE WHEN QUANTITY REACHES 3 TIMES THE QUALITY LEVEL

SALESPERSON'S OFFENSIVE STRENGTH = AVERAGE DURATION OF SALES CALLS X AVERAGE NUMBER OF SALES CALLS PER DAY

THIS EQUATION HELPS US UNDERSTAND OFFENSIVE QUALITY AND ITS LEVELS ON A PER-DAY BASIS

NOTICE THAT THE EQUATION ALSO EXPRESSES THE AVERAGE DURATION OF A SALES CALL ON A PER - DAY BASIS

THIS IS, OF COURSE A SALESPERSON'S ACTIVITY VOLUME, WHICH LEADS TO RESULTS

QUALITY

ACTIVITY VOLUME

SALESPERSON'S OFFENSIVE STRENGTH

$=$

KNOWLEDGE

SALES SKILLS

PERSONALITY

$\times$

$$\dfrac{\text{DURATION OF SALES CALL}}{\text{NUMBER OF SALES CALLS}}$$

SALESPERSON'S OFFENSIVE QUANTITY

(PER PERSON)

$=$

AVERAGE DURATION OF SALES CALL

$\times$

AVERAGE NUMBER OF SALES CALLS

$=$ TOTAL TIME SPENT ON CLIENT VISITS

$\approx$ SALESPERSON'S RESULTS

SO, WE HAVE TO FIND A WAY TO TURN WASTED TIME INTO OFFENSIVE QUANTITY

THIS IS CALLED "TIME MANAGEMENT"

WASTED TIME ?

IT'S IDLE TIME, HOURS SPENT ON THE ROAD OR IN THE OFFICE, THAT REDUCES OFFENSIVE QUANTITY

BUT THIS ISN'T THE INDIVIDUAL SALESPERSON'S FAULT. IT'S A PROBLEM THAT NEEDS TO BE ADDRESSED ON A COMPANY-WIDE BASIS

WE'RE NOT 100% THERE YET, BUT AT LEAST EVERYONE IS AWARE OF TIME MANAGEMENT NOW

I'VE BEEN TALKING ABOUT EACH SALES-PERSON'S OFFENSIVE QUANTITY.
LET'S LOOK AT THAT IN TERMS OF THE CUSTOMER

OFFENSIVE QUANTITY (CUSTOMER-DIRECTED) = AVERAGE DURATION OF EACH SALES CALL X SALES CALL FREQUENCY (INCLUDING CUMULATIVE FACTOR)

SINCE THE BATTLE AT THIS CLIENT SITE IS A LOCAL ONE, LAW NO. 1 IS APPLIED

THE OFFENSIVE QUANTITY EXPRESSES THE RELATIVE STRENGTHS OF RIVALS COMPETING FOR A CLIENT

IT HAS A CLOSE CORRELATION WITH THE NUMBER AND VOLUME OF ORDERS, OR CUSTOMER SHARE

IF YOUR OFFENSIVE QUANTITY IS GREATER THAN YOUR RIVAL'S, YOUR MARKET SHARE WILL BE LARGER, TOO.

TO REVERSE A RIVAL'S POSITION AND INCREASE YOUR SHARE OF A CLIENT'S BUSINESS YOU MUST BOOST YOUR OFFENSIVE QUANTITY

BUT IT'S IMPOSSIBLE TO INCREASE OFFENSIVE QUANTITY FOR EVERY CLIENT, NO MATTER HOW CAREFUL YOU ARE ABOUT TIME MANAGEMENT

THUS . . .
IT IS ESSENTIAL TO DECIDE WHICH CLIENTS TO WORK ON FIRST, AND TO CAPTURE THEM ONE BY ONE . . .

TO BECOME NO. 1 IN REGION A, OUR TEAM PINPONTED KEY CUSTOMERS AND APPLIED MORE OFFENSIVE QUANTITY THAN OUR RIVALS DID

BUT ARE SALES CALLS REALLY ENOUGH ?

WOULDN'T IT BE MORE PRODUCTIVE TO RAISE THE QUALITY LEVEL ?

BUT OUR SHARE <u>HAS</u> GROWN. CLIENTS KNOW WE 'RE SERIOUS WHEN OUR VISITS ARE FREQUENT AND LONG

162

THE ATTACKING QUANTITY USED BY COMPANY B IS GREATER, BUT COMPANY A HAS A TEN YEAR HISTORY OF ACCUMULATING CUSTOMERS

THE CUMULATIVE FACTOR CANNOT BE USED SIMPLISTICALLY, JUST BY MULTIPLYIING THE NUMBER OF YEARS OR MONTHS. BUT IF B WANTS TO OVERTHROW A, IT MUST INCREASE OFFENSIVE QUANTITY

$$\text{ATTACKING QUANTITIES USED ON ONE CUSTOMER} = \text{AVERAGE TIME SPENT ON EACH CUSTOMER VISIT} \times \text{NUMBER OF CUSTOMER VISITS}$$

$$\text{TEAM OR COMPANY OFFENSIVE QUANTITY} = \text{AVERAGE DURATION OF SALES CALLS} \times \left[\text{AVERAGE NUMBER OF DAILY VISITS}\right]^2$$

$$\approx \text{REGIONAL MARKET SHARE}$$

$$\approx \text{INDUSTRY SHARE}$$

TEAM OF 5

TEAM OF 10

THUS THE MAIN DIFFERENCE IN OFFENSIVE QUANTITY IS THE SIZE OF THE SALES FORCE

COMPANY	SALES CALLS	SALES FORCE	TOTAL NO. OF CALLS
A	10	10	100
B	10	5	50

COMPANY OFFENSIVE QUANTITY	VISIT DURATION	$\left[\begin{array}{c}\text{AVERAGE NUMBER OF SALES CALLS}\end{array}\right]^2$	AVERAGE TOTAL SALES CALLS PER DAY	RATIO
COMPANY A =	30 MINS ×	100^2	= 300,000	4
COMPANY B =	30 MINS ×	50^2	= 75,000	1

SUPPOSE THAT IN A PARTICULAR REGION, COMPANY A HAS A TEAM OF 10, AND COMPANY B HAS A TEAM OF 5. EACH COMPANY MAKES 10 30-MINUTE SALES CALLS PER DAY. THEN, THE OFFENSIVE QUANTITY IS EQUAL TO THE SALES FORCE RATIO $(10:5)^2$ THAT IS $(2:1)^2$, OR 4:1

THAT'S WHY OUR TEAM FOCUSED ON REGION A

OF COURSE OF COURSE CONTINUE !

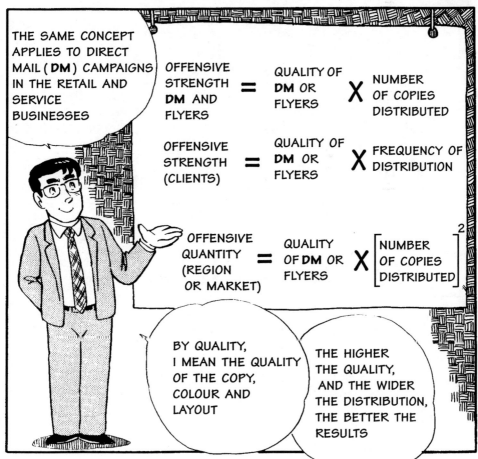

THE SAME CONCEPT APPLIES TO DIRECT MAIL (**DM**) CAMPAIGNS IN THE RETAIL AND SERVICE BUSINESSES

$$\text{OFFENSIVE STRENGTH } \textbf{DM} \text{ AND FLYERS} = \text{QUALITY OF } \textbf{DM} \text{ OR FLYERS} \times \text{NUMBER OF COPIES DISTRIBUTED}$$

$$\text{OFFENSIVE STRENGTH (CLIENTS)} = \text{QUALITY OF } \textbf{DM} \text{ OR FLYERS} \times \text{FREQUENCY OF DISTRIBUTION}$$

$$\text{OFFENSIVE QUANTITY (REGION OR MARKET)} = \text{QUALITY OF } \textbf{DM} \text{ OR FLYERS} \times \left[\text{NUMBER OF COPIES DISTRIBUTED} \right]^2$$

BY QUALITY, I MEAN THE QUALITY OF THE COPY, COLOUR AND LAYOUT

THE HIGHER THE QUALITY, AND THE WIDER THE DISTRIBUTION, THE BETTER THE RESULTS

I HOPE THAT WAS CLEAR. THIS CONCLUDES MY EXPLANATION OF THE BASICS OF THE LANCHESTER STRATEGY

THANK YOU. CONNECTIONS AREN'T GOING TO KEEP US IN BUSINESS. WE HAVE TO BE MORE SCIENTIFIC

BUT THERE'S MORE ISN'T THERE?

OH, YES! NEXT TIME I'D LIKE TO TALK ABOUT THE STRATEGY OF THE WEAK

WELL, I HAVE A GREAT DEAL OF INTEREST IN THIS STRATEGY. YOU ARE THE NO. 1 IN THAT

WELL, I MADE IT THROUGH THE FIRST PART, I HOPE THE REST GOES THIS WELL.

169

SUMMARY

Strategy and Tactics

Strategy and tactics are military terms. Strategy has been defined as "what cannot be seen," and tactics as "what can be seen." These terms should be viewed in the same way when they are used within the context of corporate competition. Strategy is a matter of planning what you are going to do and how to achieve it.

For instance, strategy embraces regional strategy, product strategy, distribution strategy, sales promotion strategy, pricing policy, and product development.

Tactics refers to the action taken to achieve a strategy. Sales activities, publicity and advertising campaigns are all tactics. Tactics should be based on strategy, but in Japan strategy has been neglected, perhaps because it cannot be seen.

However, in corporate competition, strategy holds the key to victory or defeat. The Lanchester Strategy makes this clear when it shows the distribution of strength, by assigning a value of 2 to strategy, and 1 to tactics.

In today's times, blind expenditures of effort alone will not change anything. But it is important to be mindful that no strategy, however superior, will not be successful without tactics. Unless action is taken, strategy is nothing but empty theory that never leaves the drawing board.

One major feature of the Lanchester Strategy is its scientific grasp of sales activities and publicity or advertising campaigns.

The Salesperson's Offensive Strength

Lanchester's first law applies to individual salespersons' activities, since they are waging local battles. Fighting strength, according to the first law, is expressed as

$$E \times (\text{numerical strength})$$

in this case, E represents quality. Therefore, a salesperson's "quality" is his specialized knowledge, charisma, and salesmanship.Numerical strength is his activity volume, i.e., offensive quantity. This refers to the number and duration of sales calls.

Then, if we expand the above-mentioned formula, we have

Salesperson's offensive strength = (salesperson's quality) x (offensive quantity)

Since offensive strength is the salesperson' performance, if he increases his offensive strength, his performance will also improve.

Higher priority should be given to offense than to improving quality. This is so because quality (specialized knowledge, charisma, salesmanship) is not easily raised, but quantity can be increased instantly. Even when quality remains low, if that deficiency is made up for by quantity, there will be at least some improvement in performance.

Furthermore, once quantity has been increased, i.e., the more territory that is covered, the more quality will improve. If you observe a veteran salesperson on the job, you will be convinced that this is true.

Salesperson's Offensive Quantity

A salesperson's offensive quantity is expressed by the following equation:

Salesperson's offensive quantity = (average duration of sales call) x (average number of sales calls per day)

This equation expresses the total time a salesperson spends on his clients' premises in one day.

This offensive quantity has a strong correlation with a salesperson's performance. If he increases offensive quantity, his performance increases, too.

In order to increase offensive quantity, a salesperson may:

1. Increase the number of working hours
2. Be more scrupulous about time management

However, in our aging society, it would be irresponsible to suggest that people work longer hours.

Thus, we are left with one choice — managing our time more effectively. Generally, the reasons for idle time, the cause of decreased offensive quantity, are as follows:

1. Time spent in transit

* Failure to schedule sales calls properly
* Too large a territory
* Territory too distant from base
* Salespeople not assigned to specific territories

2. Time wasted at the office

* Too many meetings or meetings that last too long
* Too much material to read
* Poorly organized reference material
* Low morale

Applying Offensive Quantity to Clients

Since the battle waged at the clients' premises is a local one, Lanchester's first law applies here.

Offensive quantity applied to clients = [average duration of sales call] x [frequency of sales calls (including cumulative factor)]

In this case, offensive quantity refers to the relative strength of rivals, i.e., their respective shares of a particular client's business. There is a strong correlation between offensive quantity and performance (number of orders or volume), i.e., the share of that client's business. To overthrow a rival, a company must invest more offensive quantity than its rival does.

However, the reversal does not happen overnight, no matter how much offensive quantity is applied to a client. Here is where the cumulative factor comes in.

Team or Company Offensive Quantity

For offensive quantity when invested by team efforts (branches, sales offices, divisions, or sections) or by an entire company, Lanchester's second law applies.

According to that law, fighting strength is expressed as:

$$E \times (\text{numerical strength})^2$$

In this case, numerical strength is the total number of sales calls made on an average day. Therefore, the offensive quantity for team efforts or entire company efforts is expressed by the following equation:

Team or company offensive quantity = (average duration of sales call per client) x (daily average total sales calls)^2

There is a close correlation between this type of offensive quantity and regional or industry share.

Members of sales forces in the same industry generally follow similar behavior patterns. The number and duration of their sales calls does not differ greatly. For that reason, increasing the sales force will have a significant effect on offensive quantity.

A company with a small sales force must pinpoint a key region, customer base, or product, and concentrate its efforts there. At the same time, it must be scrupulous about time management. If you cannot win the war, you must move ahead by winning local battles, one by one.

POSTSCRIPT

The *New Lanchester Strategy* is the first volume in a three-volume series that explains the basic principles of the strategy. It is followed by the second volume, *Strategy of the Weak* and the third, *Strategy of the Strong*

Readers who are coming into contact with the Lanchester Strategy for the first time are encouraged to read this book several times. Repetition is part of the learning process, no matter what the subject. Without a thorough understanding of the basics, it would be difficult to put these theories into practice.

Thinking back, I approached this series rather lightheartedly at first. I thought the comic-book format would be an easy one to work in, but it turned out to be more difficult than I had anticipated. This was a learning experience for me, as I collected and analyzed new reference material, and went through the trial-and-error process several times.

Furthermore, I made many unreasonable demands of my cartoonist Kenichi Sato. I am satisfied, though, that we have produced a work that is a bit different from the traditional writings on the Lanchester Strategy.

I endeavored to provide hints for applying the strategy to as many fields as possible. Unfortunately, due to time and space limitations, I have not been entirely successful. Since the retail and service sectors have been particularly neglected in this book, I plan to publish further volumes dealing with the needs of those sectors.

In closing, I would like to thank Mr. Takahashi of Wako Printing Company and his staff, Mr. Miura of the CUE Research Institute, Editor-in-Chief Homma and Mr. Sakuma of the Japan Management Consultants Association, and the many others who assisted me.

Shinichi Yano

ALSO AVAILABLE FROM LANCHESTER PRESS:

NEW LANCHESTER STRATEGY
Volume I by Shinichi Yano

First Volume of Yano's pioneering *New Lanchester Strategy*. Deals with the derivation of Lanchester's equations of combat and applications to marketing strategy. Chapters include basic Lanchester strategy, Laws No.1 & 2, market share patterns, principle of one-point concentration, strategy and tactics. Over 90,000 copies of the original version sold in Japan.

Softcover, 174 pp, 5 chapters.   ISBN 1-57321-000-5. $17.95

NEW LANCHESTER STRATEGY
Volume 2 by Shinichi Yano
Sales and Marketing Strategy for the Weak

Second volume of Shinichi Yano's pioneering work on "Lanchester" marketing strategy. Differentiation strategy, local and single battles, downstream campaign and principle of "one-point concentration." Deals with tactics and strategy for the weak company, and new product introduction. Over 50,000 copies of the original version sold in Japan.

Softcover, 170 pp, 6 chapters.   ISBN 1-57321-004-8. $17.95

NEW LANCHESTER STRATEGY
Volume 3 by Shinichi Yano
Sales and Marketing Strategy for the Strong

Third volume of Shinichi Yano's pioneering work on "Lanchester" marketing strategy. Matching operations, Wide-area battles, Stochastic battles, Remote and Comprehensive battles. Inducement operations and the general response of the market leader to market share pressure by rival companies. Over 40,000 copies of the original version sold in Japan.

Softcover, 174 pp, 6 chapters.   ISBN 1-57321-005-6. $17.95

ALSO AVAILABLE FROM LANCHESTER PRESS:

ISO 9000 FOR EXECUTIVES
Understand the Fastest Growing Program to Impact
American Industry and Commerce.
by Dr. Jack E. Small

This important new book, written from the perspective of a senior executive,
describes the background and application of the ISO 9000 standards.
It includes chapters on all aspects for understanding the most important
quality tool available for companies in North America. This book is based on
the experience of Dr. Small in taking over 150 IBM world wide sites to ISO
9000 registration.

Hardcover, 225 pp, 10 chapters, 29 illustrations, appendix, index
ISBN 1-57321-001-3. $25.95

HI - TECH EQUIPMENT RELIABILITY
A Practical Guide for Engineers and the Engineering Manager
by Dr. Vallabh H. Dhudshia

Today's highly competitive, global marketplace demands an optimum level of
equipment reliability. To achieve world-class reliability, everyone in an
organization must participate or have adequate knowledge of the reliability
discipline. This book is a guidebook on reliabiity for design, manufacturing and
service engineers, management and all others who can actively contribute to
equipment reliability. Dr. Dhudshia's book was developed from a lecture series
presented at SEMATECH while on assignment from Texas Instruments.

Hardcover, 140 pp, 14 chapters, appendix, index.
ISBN 1-57321-003-X. $26.95

ALSO AVAILABLE FROM LANCHESTER PRESS:

THE LANCHESTER LEGACY, 1895 - 1931
Volume I by C. S. Clark

The official historian of the Lanchester Car Register tells the fascinating story
of the Lanchester brothers, Frederick, George and Frank. The story has been
developed from collected documents and photographs, many of them previ-
ously unpublished. Described are important inventions such as the disc brake,
four-wheel drive, fuel-injection, turbo-charging and more.
A must for all automobile enthusiasts.

Hardcover, large format 8.5 x 11 ins, 24 chapters, 272 photographs,
35 illustrations, index, appendix. ISBN 0-905949-30-7 $45.00

THE LANCHESTER LEGACY, A Celebration of Genius
Volume III Edited by John Fletcher

Fred Lanchester was one of the first engineers to evolve a theory of flight,
and there are chapters on aerodynamics and the use of aircraft in warfare, He
devised a mathematical theory of military strategy, the N-Square law, which is
the foundation stone of operations research. This has been developed in
Japan as a business strategy, and one of the leading exponents writes for the
first time in English on its application. Lanchester wrote on optics, building
construction and many engineering firsts; he published books on the theory
of dimensions, the musical scale, and several volumes of poetry. Lanchester
applied for over 400 patents, 236 of which were granted; they are all listed.

Hardcover, large format 8.5 x 11 ins, 20 chapters, 18 photographs,
77 illustrations, index, appendix. ISBN 0-905949-47-1 $49.00

ALSO AVAILABLE FROM LANCHESTER PRESS:

AIRCRAFT IN WARFARE, The Dawn of the Fourth Arm
by F. W. Lanchester
New edition of Lanchester's classic 1916 work

New edition, complete with new photographic material from the Imperial War
Museum and the RAF Museum England. This pioneering work describes the use
of aircraft in all aspects of warfare at the time of WW I. Forms the basis of
the science of Operations Research. A must for all aeronautical enthusiasts.

Hardcover, 243 pp, 19 chapters, 21 photograps, 21 illustrations, index.
ISBN 1-57321-002-1 $24.95

ISO 9000 FOR BETTER BUSINESS
Using ISO 9000 as a Foundation for Total Quality Management.
by Dr. Jack E. Small

How to implement and build on the ISO 9000 and related quality systems to
get to a higher level of profitable business. Includes the new Malcolm Baldrige
National Quality Award, and Total Quality Management programs.
Softcover, 152 pages, 7 chapters, 23 illustrations, appendix, index.
ISBN 1-57321-013-7 $19.95

JAPAN INC Volume 2
An Introduction to the Japanese Economy
by Shotaro Ishinomori

This second volume of Ishinomori's legendary Japan Inc. deals with the
attempted takeover of a Tokyo bank by a US bank, the state of transplant
car factories in the US, and the attempted theft of software operating
systems. Also deals with sunspot theory economic cycles the Kondratieff
Wave and Yoshimura agricultural goods economic cycle.
Softcover, 303 pages, 5 chapters, in Manga (comic) style.
ISBN 1-57321-006-4 $14.95

FAX ORDER FORM TO: 408-732-7723
LANCHESTER PRESS INC.
P.O. BOX 60621 SUNNYVALE, CA 94086
http://www.lanchester.com

Name_____ Tel_____

Addr_____

_____

City_____ State____ Zip_____

ITEM	Qty	Price	TOTAL
New Lanchester Strategy Vol. 1		$17.95	
New Lanchester Strategy Vol. 2		$17.95	
New Lanchester Strategy Vol. 3		$17.95	
Lanchester Legacy Vol. I		$49.00	
Lanchester Legacy Vol. III		$49.00	
Aircraft in Warfare		$24.95	
ISO 9000 for Executives		$25.95	
Hi-Tech Equipment Reliability		$26.95	
ISO 9000 for Better Business		$19.95	
Japan Inc. Volume 2		$14.95	
1st class $4.00 first book add $.75 each extra book Overseas add $4.00 each book	Subtotal		
	Shipping		
Book Rate: $2.00 first book add $0.75 each extra book	CA Tax		
	TOTAL		

VISA_____   MC_____   Check_____ Money Order_____

Cardholder. |_|_|_|_|_|_|_|_|_|_|_|_|_|_|_|_|_|_|_|_|_|_|_|_|_|_|_|

Number. |_|_|_|_|_| - |_|_|_|_|_| - |_|_|_|_|_| - |_|_|_|_| Exp___/___

Signature_____